The Story of the Storm of October 1987

HURRICANE FORCE

The Story of the Storm of October 1987

HURRICANE FORCE

George Hill

COLLINS
8 Grafton Street, London W1
1988

TO
THE DESIGNER,
WHO NEVER GETS A DEDICATION,
BUT WITHOUT WHOM THIS BOOK
WOULD NOT EXIST

William Collins Sons & Co. Ltd
London · Glasgow · Sydney · Auckland · Toronto · Johannesburg
First published 1988
Copyright © George Hill 1988

Typeset by Ace Filmsetting Ltd, Frome, Somerset
Printed and bound by William Collins Sons & Co. Ltd, Glasgow

ISBN 0 00 219374 4

CONTENTS

ACKNOWLEDGEMENTS

A book of this kind is necessarily heavily dependent on press reports: not only those directly quoted in the text, but also many more which have served as hints and leads. In addition to helping us in this way, several local papers kindly allowed us to forage through their rich stocks of photographs – as did the National Trust.

In particular I am grateful to the *Jersey Weekly Post, Bournemouth Evening Echo, Isle of Wight County Press, Mid-Sussex Times, Brighton Evening Argus, Hastings and St Leonards Observer, Windsor and Maidenhead Observer, Dover Express, Eastern Daily Press, East Anglian Daily Times,* and *North Norfolk News* – and of course to the *Sevenoaks Chronicle*, Bob Ogley and *"In the Wake of the Hurricane"*.

Among national publications, I am especially indebted to *The Observer*, for allowing me to quote at length from Douglas Nye's dramatic personal narrative, and to *The Daily Telegraph, The Independent, Daily Mail, Le Monde, De Telegraaf* of Amsterdam and *New Scientist*: and most of all to that still-unfallen oak, *The Times* – in particular to its library (for its resources) and its features department (for their patience).

I am also grateful to many witnesses of the storm – to all of those named in the text and a great many more – and to others who generously spared much time trying to help me grasp Bernoulli's principle and the like. In particular Ian James, of the Department of Meteorology, Reading University; Sam Webb, of the Department of Architecture, Canterbury College of Art; Dougal Gonsal, Chief Engineer of the London Borough of Camden, and Simon Potter of the Jack and Jill Windmills Society. But these are only a few of very many, whose patience and willingness to tell their stories made the book a real pleasure to compile.

In a story whose list of characters runs into several hundred, I have not been able to double-check every reference. I may have introduced errors of my own. Dust and ashes in all cases.

My research assistant, Margaret Pearson, took a great deal of the hard grind off my hands in the sections on parks, gardens and agriculture. Among the staff of Collins, I am particularly indebted to my Editor, Francesca Dow, and to Crispin Fisher, head of the natural history department, for steering me away from some of my more haywire ideas; and to Caroline Hill, the designer.

All times mentioned in the text are British Summer Time or its equivalent (for this one month of the year, clocks in France and England most conveniently ran neck and neck). Miles are statute miles, whether by land or sea, and degrees are Fahrenheit, unless specified. Except where the effect seemed excessively artificial, I have followed the convention of using the past tense – "he said, etc . . ." – when lifting quotations from other sources, and the present – "She says, etc . . ." when reporting what people told me.

CHAPTER 1

AS WE WERE

"In Hertford, Hereford and Hampshire,
hurricanes hardly happen."
(Alan Jay Lerner: *My Fair Lady*)

Out in the Channel, there was hardly a breath of wind. Early in the morning of Thursday, October 15, 1987, the English three-masted training ship *Malcolm Miller* set sail for home from Cherbourg, in Northern France. The sea lay idly in a monochrome calm as she passed the marina, one of the largest concentrations of pleasure craft in any of the Channel ports, where several million pounds worth of yachting hardware was congregated under the apparently infallible shelter of Napoleon's huge granite sea walls.

The *Miller* had sixty miles to sail to Cowes, her destination for the night. The weather was in a sullen, still mood all along her course, and across ten thousand miles of southern England, where homes, churches, gardens, schools and woodlands were spread out in the unthinking security of a coldish autumn morning. The complex services of one of the most affluent and densely populated corners of the world hummed with all their usual smoothness – almost unperceived by those who enjoyed them, except in their omissions. Frustrated commuters on the lines to London Bridge might groan as the train drew in six minutes late for the third morning running. British Telecom subscribers might ring to complain that they had stayed in all morning waiting for the repairman, but he had never turned up. Outpatients at Thanet hospitals might grumble about the collapse of the National Heath service when the doctor turned up late to start her list.

Rain was forecast, and over much of the south during the afternoon it obeyed the weatherman's prediction and began to fall, long and hard in places. This was something to receive with resignation, too. The weather had been perverse all year, to an almost unnatural degree. There had been snowfalls, rainstorms and droughts far out of the usual range: one August gale in East Anglia had been nicknamed "the storm of the century" by the local press.

A few miles north of the coast for which the *Miller* was quietly heading, the hilltop crescent of ancient beeches at Churchill's old estate of Chartwell were scarcely beginning as yet to take on the autumn colours which are the special glory of an English beechwood. The largest sweet chestnut in the country and the gigantic cedar of Lebanon beside it in the Pleasure Ground at Petworth, Sussex, moved their boughs gently in the winds they had been used to for 150 years. The deep forest rides of Knole Park in Kent, where it was still possible to imagine oneself in a medieval England of clearings in a vast enveloping woodland, were almost deserted now on an out-of-season weekday. At Sheffield Park, near Lewes, the long beds of fragile blue gentians which had become one of the chief autumn showpieces of a garden famous for its autumm phase, were about to come into flower, shaded by silver maples.

In Bexhill, Marjorie Doddington was filling her deep freeze with sausage rolls and shelled prawns for her daughter Marion's wedding reception on Saturday. In Edenbridge, Kent, the McDonagh family was preparing for a double christening at the weekend, in which the clan would be gathering from as far afield as Wyoming and Sydney. Down wooded lanes in the village of Ardingley, Sussex, Frances Esposito was wondering whether the baby about to arrive would be a girl this time.

In the music room of the Prince Regent's Pavilion in Brighton, encircled by its elms, a cleaner was running a carpet sweeper over the palace's latest adornment, a brand-new £90,000 blue and gold carpet, sixty feet across, a reproduction of the long-destroyed original of the 1820s.

High above Brighton, the white sails of Jack and Jill, the twin windmills on the backbone of Clayton Down, stood up against the clouds like a dainty greetings card view. Near Canterbury, Nick Marx, a keeper at Howlett's Zoo, was casting an expert but wary eye over the tigers Khan and Zabel, a male and female in their prime, each weighing about four hundredweight; he had known Khan since he was a cub. In West Wittering, a riding horse called Amber was looking poorly, and its owner was making up her mind to call the vet.

In Hastings, Jimmie Read, winch-man for the fishing boats which trawl by hand off the open beach, was probably taking it easy, as it was his turn for a night's duty that evening. In Windsor, Mrs Patricia Bellwood, a social services consultant from Newcastle-on-Tyne, was preparing a lecture she was to deliver in Reading on the controversial subject of child abuse. In Hove, Mrs Beryl Agha was possibly out shopping for dinner for her teenage daughters, Melissa and Michelle. In Canvey Island, the postman Mrs Sylvia Brown was no doubt out early delivering the mail.

In Barking Creek, the small coaster *Sumnia* was preparing to take the tide down river for a routine run to Shoreham, to pick up a load of grain. Her master was a Belfast man, David Birch. The name of her mate was Ron Horlock, and there were four others in the crew. In Harwich, 38 Tamil immigrants detained on board the disused ferry *Earl William* while their applications to enter the United Kingdom were interminably scrutinised by the Home Office kicked their heels and gazed out over the Essex mudflats.

In London, 108 anxious citizens were on tenterhooks, waiting for the outcome of 54 cases set down to be heard next day at the Law Courts in the Strand. The young lions of the Big Bang Stock Exchange were riding the highest bull market in history as if there was no tomorrow. The statue of the old socialist Fenner Brockway stood in Red Lion Square gesticulating towards the dull sky as if calling for retribution on such profligacy. The statue was waiting for its subject's centenary celebrations a few months away: has any other celebrity come so close to celebrating his hundredth birthday in a London park at the foot of his own statue?

All along the Mall, the plane trees were standing upright, and there was no more than a glaze of damp on the royal red tarmac. In Kew Gardens, the Tree of Heaven which had been planted in 1837 beside its exact contemporary, William IV's doric pillared temple, now overshadowed the building which had once overshadowed it.

On St Andrew's Hill, Clerkenwell, the features editor of *The Observer* was thinking that Douglas Nye, the paper's motoring correspondent, was cutting things a bit fine again in delivering his article for next Sunday's edition. David Sore, a clerk in a City solicitors' office, got into his 1980 Fiesta to drive to work that morning, with no inkling of the danger it stood in. The sculptor Antony Gormley was preoccupied with the irritations of a delayed move from his ramshackle lean-to in Brixton to a newly-refurbished studio in Peckham. As for me, I was fretting in Kentish Town, at a loss to decide what best to do with the golden enigma of a five-weeks' sabbatical from work, which had to be taken shortly.

Along the Darent valley in Kent, and far more widely throughout the Weald and East Anglia, council workers, police and firemen were polishing up on their emergency plan procedures, in case of the floods which imminently threatened after unprecedented torrents of rain. And at about 3 pm in Bracknell, Berkshire, the senior duty forecaster of the Meteorological Office was sitting down with the abstracted summaries provided by Bracknell's seven-year-old Cyber 205 computer, to prepare the afternoon's synoptic review, on which all the day's broadcast weather bulletins would be based.

The computer showed a moderate but deepening depression with a centre of 970 millibars just to the north of Cape Finisterre, in Spain. The data made it difficult to be certain how fast it would deepen, and which way it would go. "Whoever happened to be on duty on 15 October was going to face what was likely to be the severest test of his career", the official report to the Secretary of State for Defence observed four months later: but that was with hindsight.

That was how all these things were then. Within 24 hours, the Cherbourg marina was driftwood, the carpet was spoilt, the wedding reception was off, the christening was still on, and Mrs Esposito knew the answer to the question she had been asking herself. Marx and the tiger had stood face to face in unforeseen confrontation, the horse had changed its name, and the *Sumnia* was at the bottom of the Channel. The beeches, the oaks, the elms, the planes, the chestnut, the cedar and the tree of heaven were mere pathetic wreckage. Mr Read, Mrs Bellwood, Mrs Agha and Mrs Brown were all dead, and so were fifteen others. The duty officer at Bracknell knew he had got things wrong.

There were few on land or sea who had had any inkling of what was about to happen. A few amateur weathermen claimed later that they had foreseen the coming storm, but few of them got any closer to the truth than the Met Office had done. Eight-year-old Matthew Jones of Heathfield, Sussex, looked out of the window before going off to school, and said: "Those clouds are thunderheads. We're going to have a hurricane tonight."

The three cats belonging to Miss Ursula Vaughan Williams in north London seemed to feel something in the air, for they spent the day fighting and rampaging round the house in a way she had never seen before. She wrote to *The Observer* to say she was sure they had had a premonition. Nora Bale of Box Hill noticed that her three dogs were unusually restless, whimpering and running in and out of her caravan.

If these animals did have foreknowledge of the storm, they were unusual, for *The Observer* letter induced me to ask everyone I spoke to whether they had noticed any unusual prior behaviour among animals, and I was disappointed to find that most had not.

But in Newlyn and Falmouth and other West Country ports, onlookers did notice an unusual sight. Fishing boats from the French trawler fleet were coming in to lie for the night in sheltered waters – eight or ten in Falmouth, a score or more in Newlyn. They are powerful boats, used to riding out any ordinary gale; their crews are never inclined to waste valuable earning time by leaving the fishing grounds unnecessarily.

In the Falmouth harbourmaster's office they looked out at the big trawlers crowding into the narrow inner harbour, and one of the staff said: "It has to be pretty bad for the French to start coming in for shelter. Maybe they know something we don't."

And in Bungay in Suffolk, a craftsman got down to a job he had been meaning to do for weeks, and overhauled an old barometer that a customer had brought in for repair. Last thing at night, he took another look at it to make sure that it was behaving now. When he saw what it was reading, he shook his head, promised himself to have another look at it tomorrow, and went up to bed.

CHAPTER 2

DIRTY WEATHER

*"For hot, cold, moist, and dry, four Champions fierce
Strive here for Maistrie, and to Battel bring
Their embryon Atoms."*
(John Milton: *Paradise Lost*, Book 2)

Five hundred miles to the south, a doleful procession of ships was slowly making its way past Cape Finisterre. A German long-distance tugboat was towing two larger ships "in tandem" from Europe to the knackers' yards of Taiwan. It is a curiosity of world economics that can make it profitable to tow ships halfway round the world simply to be torn to pieces, but the trade is a thriving one.

The larger of the two ships making their slow way to oblivion was a high-sided snub-nosed vessel, surprisingly modern in its outline in the circumstances. It was painted in what had once been a garish orange-and-white livery, now streaked with rust and deeply scarred. The only patches of fresh paint on its sides marked the place where its name had been picked out: *Flushing Range*, not a name to catch the eye.

But the name was only a recent disguise, painted up to obscure a much more notorious one. The ship was in fact the ferry *Herald of Free Enterprise*, which had capsized off Zeebrugge seven months before, with the loss of 193 lives. The bitterness of that disaster had been intensified by the fact that the ship's loss had been wholly avoidable. The bow doors through which cars and lorries would drive aboard into her vast open car deck had been left open when she left harbour. The seaman whose job it was to close them had overslept, and it was no-one's clear responsibility to make sure that the job had been done.

As soon as the *Herald* gathered speed, hundreds of tons of water were scooped up into the car deck, and the ship overturned in seconds. Passengers and crew were left struggling to escape in darkness through a maze of internal passages. Many acts of heroism and desperation had been done in those steel alleyways. If the ship had sailed a few yards further, she would have gone down in deep water and almost all of the 530 souls on board would have drowned. The rescue operation mounted by the Belgian authorities was a model of efficiency, with helicopters on the scene within minutes.

Few travellers would have relished going to sea in that ship again. After she was raised, the owners sold her for scrap – a decision which cost them about £7 million, because the insurers pointed out that her condition would quite well have allowed her to be repaired, and refused to pay her full insured value of £20 million. But P & O did not want the floating reminder of past incompetence to exist at all under their ownership or anybody else's. Her proud political name was painted out, and she had set out on her last journey about ten days earlier. There was a persistent legend in Britain that there were some bodies still lying undiscovered on board, but this was denied.

The motion of a ship under tow is uncomfortable: instead of the healthy drumming of the engines there is only the spongy tug of the steel cable as it comes taut between wave-crests. As the weather worsened, the stresses on the cable increased, and at last it parted. The wind blew the ship's bow to one side, and she drifted awkwardly sideways to the waves, back in the direction of Zeebrugge.

The weather was too bad for the tug to get a line onto the *Herald*, which had no crew aboard, and for five days the disgraced ship drifted before the gale. The dreary lounges and assembly areas, echoing only with the sound of waves and the rising wind – littered with the debris of loss and rescue and dark with silt – were vacant, unless they were patrolled by the ghosts of those who had died there.

The storm waves which slapped heavily against the *Herald*'s side were not as cold as those which had flowed through her off Zeebrugge. The Bay of Biscay is a reservoir of warmth at this time of year, and it is the warmth which makes it such a notorious breeder of bad weather. Our gale was manufactured just about at the point where the ship went adrift, from the conjunction of two elements. The Biscay effect was the first of these.

Like the hot floor of a saucepan, the warm surface of the sea, retaining the heat of the summer longer than the surrounding land, warms the air above it. Growing lighter as it warms up, this air rises. Cooler air is drawn in to replace it, one particle pulling its neighbour, for nature abhors a vacuum. The prevailing north-westerly airstream tends to carry these vast balloons of rising air across France and Britain, and they draw cooler air in under their skirts as they go.

They do so by a very roundabout process. An inexorable natural force forms these low pressure areas into the huge spiral eddies familiar from weather maps. In a simpler universe, one might expect the cool air to flow straight to the centre. In practice, the process creates highly complex and rather durable self-sustaining rotating structures almost like primitive life-forms. The force that brings this about was first described in the 1830s by the French mathematician Gustave–Gaspard Coriolis. He was a lover of billiards, and also wrote a definitive treatise on the graceful mechanical processes involved in that game.

The bodies of moving air may be invisible, but they have their own mass and momentum – which are considerable, because they are so large. In fact, supertankers are feathers by comparison. The whole process is laid out on the revolving globe, whose surface is moving round like a fairground roundabout. At the poles, close to its centre line, the ground is hardly moving at all. At the equator, it is moving round at thousands of miles an hour.

A mass of air near the equator, carried along eastwards with the earth's surface, is already charged with a powerful eastward momentum; the low-pressure area further north is also moving east, but less fast. If the air mass moves to fill it, its momentum will make it overshoot ahead of its target, like a stone thrown from a moving train. Air moving south from the colder regions further north has less inherent momentum than its target, and will pass behind the low-pressure area – to the west of it. Thus an anticlockwise spiral motion is set up.

If the air had the sense to adjust its aim, it would reach the target in no time. But it does not, and the diversion causes it to travel hundreds of miles unnecessarily, and to move much faster than it needs to. As it comes nearer the centre, with all its existing momentum, the air tends to increase its speed. The tighter it circles, the more its momentum turns into speed – like a skater spinning faster and faster by drawing her arms inwards.

Like a living thing, a depression grows weak if it is deprived of nourishment, and gathers new strength after a good meal. Its diet is warmth and moisture. Warmth makes the balloon of rising air rise all the more strongly, and water vapour can be converted to warmth in its digestive processes.

That mild, sultry air over Biscay supplied both warmth and moisture. Rising air becomes less dense, and so less able to retain water vapour. As the vapour turns into rain, it passes new strength into the air.

In cookery – which is essentially weather operating on a small scale, and seasoned to taste – one often notices what a great quantity of heat has to go into a saucepan to turn already boiling water into steam. That heat is needed to lift the water molecules into the livelier condition of vapour. When vapour turns back into liquid, that same heat is released. In a depression, this released heat warms the air. The warmth of the air strengthens the upward current which drives the depression.

All this is everyday stuff. The Biscay effect launches depressions towards us all the year round in this way. Another factor was needed to turn a robust Biscay depression into a killer.

In the warm, moist tropics, all these processes can happen much more energetically. A tropical hurricane works with the same kind of machinery, but develops into a tighter, fiercer spiral swirling much higher into the atmosphere, and expending a stupendous amount of energy. In parts of the world too poor to raise adequate defences, it can kill 100,000 people at a stroke.

Hurricane Floyd was on its last legs on Wednesday, October 14. It had been cooked up 4,000 miles away from Biscay, south-west of Cuba, and had whirled across Miami, Florida, before wandering out to sea again on Monday and Tuesday, and beginning to lose impetus. A cool stretch of sea can quickly cut off a hurricane's source of fuel. But the air which had gushed up the hurricane's huge chimney reached the lid of the saucepan and spread out under it, seven miles high, at speeds as great as 200 mph.

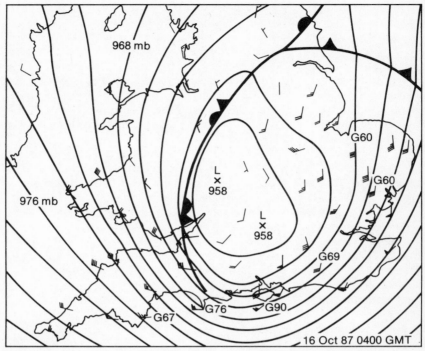

The peak of the storm, at 5 am British Summer Time. The centre of the depression over the Cotswolds, and the gale streaming round to the east and south. The "arrows" mark the direction of wind, and their "tails" indicate its strength, not counting gusts. A steady wind of almost 60 mph is shown blowing on the coast from Wight to Harwich.

This was not an unusual thing either. There is a strong easterly airflow at these heights almost all the time. Usually, however, there are a number of saucepans simmering in mid-Atlantic, which divert and cool down any particularly potent jet of air which may head towards Europe at high level. On this occasion the way happened to be clear; in fact, clockwise systems to the south and anticlockwise ones to the north actually helped to waft the jet on its way.

All this had been seen by weather forecasters. A slow-moving high-pressure zone was lying over the European mainland, and it was clear that there would be turbulence when the two forces met. There was also a chance that the javelin of air aimed at north Europe might pass over the top of a depression moving at lower level in the same direction.

If that happens, it is possible for the two systems to latch together in ways which meteorologists understand in theory, but in practice still find hard to predict. The high-level air passing overhead can reinforce the upward

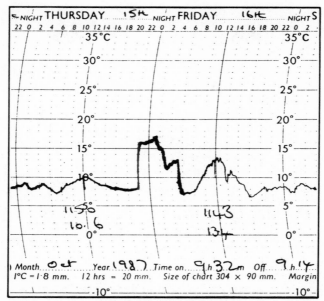

Midnight the warmest moment of the day: temperature record from the Met Office's Bracknell headquarters, showing the abrupt temperature rise as the warm front arrived there, and the fall as colder air flowed in from the west. Temperatures Celsius, times GMT.

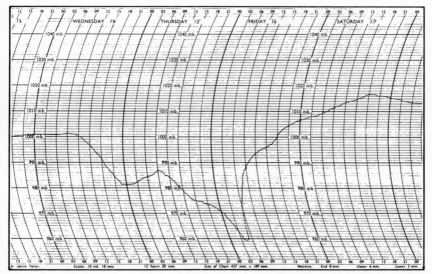

The centre of the depression passes: the barometer at Bracknell shows the long fall in pressure before the storm, followed by a sudden leap coinciding with the arrival of the strongest winds.

forces in the depression, as if by taking a lid off it, and can dramatically increase its energy. It can also speed it up and change its course. A linked system of this kind is called a "bomb" by American forecasters.

All major forecasting agencies in Europe had been giving loud warnings for days of storms later in the week. All, including the British, continued to do so to the end. But the forecasts that went out over the British media and to Met Office subscribers on the evening itself crucially under-played the risk of winds, and stressed the danger of floods instead.

Their failure was highlighted by a chance remark by the hapless Michael Fish, who in the 1.25 pm television weather forecast on BBC 1 inadvertently but irrevocably christened the tempest which was about to break by saying: "Earlier on today, apparently a woman rang the BBC and said she heard that there was a hurricane on the way. Well, if you are watching, don't worry, there isn't. . ."

In justice to the miserable man, it must be added that he went on: "But having said that, actually the weather will become very windy, but most of the strong winds incidentally will be down over Spain and across into France as well, but there is a vicious-looking area of low pressure on our doorstep nevertheless".

This buttery of "buts" was not wrong: but it was a long way short of being right enough. And 24 hours later what the nation wanted was a scapegoat, not a rationalisation. It was undeniable that the Met Office's emergency reports of extraordinary winds had not gone out even to its specialist customers like airlines and ambulance services until a mere hour or so before the blow fell.

Successful forecasting depends on information, and the storm came towards us from a direction where our information-gathering defences were thin.

At noon on Wednesday, the point of lowest pressure in the storm was 300 miles west of Finisterre, and an unremarkable 978 millibars deep. But it was moving fast. By six in the evening it was halfway across Biscay and had deepened rapidly to 963 millibars. By nine at night, it was about to arrive over Brittany. At 958 millibars, it was now very deep indeed. The ratchet between the upper and lower systems was in place. Ahead of them lay an ocean of exceptionally cool, still air. When they met, the contrasts of heat and pressure would be so sharp that violent collision would be inevitable.

The forecasters had foreseen most of this, too. But it was not easy to predict the exact time and place of the meeting between two systems, one fast-moving, the other slow-moving, and both erratic.

The science of forecasting is to some extent caught in a trough at present between two technologies. In the past, weather ships and messages from other passing vessels ("ships of opportunity") were the mainstay of maritime observation. Since the 1960s satellites have come into use, gazing down at the atmosphere from hundreds of miles above it. They send down huge quantities of data about how the weather looks from above. But they cannot yet report on what is happening inside the atmosphere as effectively as a ship can, through surface observation and the release of balloons which send back information about every level of the upper air as they rise through it.

Even politicians have long been aware that forecasting is a task that can only be done on an international scale. Europe's weather-forecasting is a fully coordinated international effort. But with the advent of satellites, governments have begun to look more sceptically on the older and more costly technology of weather ships. To be sure of having a ship on station all the time, two ships have to be committed to the job, so that each can come home for refits at intervals. The number of weather ships has steadily declined.

Once there were eight such ships in the eastern Atlantic: now there are three. Earlier last year, the French gave due notice and withdrew their ship from "Point Romeo", 700 miles out in the Atlantic north-west of Finisterre. France's partners took no steps to fill the gap: our own Met Office had been forced to contribute to the cash-limit economies imposed throughout the Civil Service, and had no incentive to step in. Britain keeps a ship on station at "Point Lima", 500 miles west of the Clyde, and there is a Soviet ship at "Point Charlie", still further north.

Most of our weather comes across "Point Lima" on its way to us: it was unlucky that this particular dose came from where "Romeo" used to be. There happened to be only one "ship of opportunity" in the area at the time.

How much sense the forecaster can make of the mountains of raw data sent down by the satellites depends crucially on the capacity of his computer. The Met Office's seven-year-old computer at Bracknell was already due to be replaced in a few months' time, and was smaller in capacity than the one used by the French weather service.

The moment was also unlucky because there was a Civil Service strike in France on Thursday. This meant that some crucial observations from France failed to reach Britain in the night.

Britain's senior forecaster was therefore at a disadvantage in several ways when he sat down in Bracknell at 3 pm on Wednesday and considered what the evening's forecasts should say. There is still an element of intuition involved at this point in the process, and the post-mortem reports judged that he had used his intuition more timidly than the French.

But he had a more difficult job to do. There was no doubt that exceptionally strong winds would be coming across France, Belgium, Holland and the Channel. The southern edge of the depression, with its warm, moist winds streaming up across the cold low-pressure zone, was certainly going to go that way. French forecasters could say "Don't panic, but put up your shutters and stay indoors", in full confidence that no one would be able accuse them afterwards of having cried wolf.

But in Britain there was no such certainty. The information available at the time indicated that the centre of the depression would pass over London. If it had, London would have had a quiet night, with strongish westerlies coming with the dawn as the "still centre" moved away. Instead, the low-pressure point passed 80 miles further west, and part of the 150-mile wide band of hurricane-force winds came across the eastern counties.

When in doubt, do you give warning of the worst option, or the most likely one ? The Met Office has a policy of ironing doubts out of its forecasts, so that instead of announcing that there is a 60 per cent chance of rain and a 10 per cent chance of wind – as forecasters do in the USA, for instance – they plump for the likeliest scenario, on the principle that the public is easily confused by alternatives.

On the night, all the emergency services in southern England were on the look-out for rain, because of the risk of floods. So the forecasters were preoccupied with making sure that everyone was fully alerted to that. In a short news-slot, it was the wind which got squeezed out. But the weather did not listen to the forecasts.

Some few weatherwise individuals in Britain were able to boast afterwards that they had read the signs better than the Met Office did. Mr J. Ritchie of Littlehampton peered out at the evening sky and advised his wife to bring in any plants she was particularly fond of from the greenhouse. The plants were saved, but the Ritchies spent much of the next day "sweeping the greenhouse off the lawn".

And at much the same time as the schooner *Malcolm Miller* was ploughing her way under reduced sail into the sheltered waters of the Solent, the smaller two-masted cadet ship *Royalist* – manned mainly by younger boys in their mid-teens – was passing Portland Bill 50 miles to the West, on a passage towards Poole which would have meant that she would still have been at sea for much of the night.

"The master and I were not satisfied with what the forecasts were saying", says David Norman, sailing master and second-in-command of the 110-ton brig. "Both of us are foreign-going master mariners and we did our own forecasting. After the 1400 hours shipping forecast we decided that with such a very young and inexperienced crew the most prudent action was to scuttle into Weymouth. We got there at about 1600 hours, and we didn't regret it."

In Spain and Portugal, the storm had already arrived. In Portugal, the river Lima, running into the Atlantic near Oporto, suffered its worst flood this century, causing damage estimated at £100 million and claiming at least ten lives. Six people were drowned and two children injured as trees and buildings in the area collapsed in 80-mph gusts. The Spanish fishing fleet had been warned in forecasts from Tuesday onwards to run for shelter, and most were safe in the estuary at El Ferrol; they were even reported to have found the storm rather an anti-climax. One man was drowned on Thursday night in La Coruña, nearby. A train from Madrid heading for the coast was blown off the rails, and several passengers were injured. There were also gales on the opposite side of the country, but the Mediterranean is a different kitchen to the Atlantic in this context.

Out across the face of the Bay of Biscay, under the shadow of the twin weather systems now meshing into one, a host of seagulls were wheeling, waiting for that mysterious seasonal message which sends them off each year towards their ocean wintering grounds far to the south. With dark grey heads and distinctive pointed black wing ends, they were Sabine's Gulls, a rare sight in Britain.

Except when they congregate to breed, they prefer to fly singly or in small flocks. Small, but with the endurance to bear long periods of harsh weather on the wing, they were on the point of heading southward when the irresistible force of the storm broke, and carried them north faster than their best efforts could take them south. They were borne helplessly into unknown territories, carried like scraps of white paper before the gale.

CHAPTER 3

"UN VERITABLE OURAGAN..."

"Long before we saw the sea, its spray was on our lips, and it showered salt rain upon us..."
(Charles Dickens: *David Copperfield*)

Le Monde, that great newspaper, expresses its Gallic sense of what is fitting as much by what it leaves out as by what it puts in. On the day after the storm, when the British press was overflowing with ardent British raptures of dismay and self-congratulation, *Le Monde* dealt with the business in one column on an inside page, under its regular laconic catch-all heading, *"Catastrophes"*.

Apart from a justifiably smug reference to the small number of casualties in France, which it attributed to the ample warnings of the approaching gale given there, the report was factual and curt. Almost half the column was taken up with a gracefully-turned piece from its correspondent in London, describing the reaction of Londoners as they woke up to power cuts and streets blocked by fallen trees. In tones of only slightly patronising good-will, it depicted the compatriots of Major Thompson and Phileas Fogg turning out in their inexplicably public-spirited British way to help open up the streets and let the traffic through.

The truth was that the utmost ferocity of the gale had fallen not on England but on France – though only on the edge of the country. The highest wind recorded anywhere in connection with the gale was the 134-mph gust measured at Pointe du Roc, near Mont St Michel, at 1.30 am by British Summer Time. The swathe of damage reached inland as far as Paris itself. Several major provincial towns in Brittany were still without electricity supplies when *Le Monde* went to press, and were to remain so for some time afterwards.

As for the events of the night before in Britain itself, a straightforward news report might have been expected to refer to the large number of deaths, and to the unprecedented destruction of woodlands. Neither of these was mentioned in the report from London, which dwelt almost exclusively on the characteristic team spirit displayed by the British. It was not until several days after the storm that the paper began to carry reports fully acknowledging that something serious in its consequences and dramatic in itself – *"un véritable ouragan"* – had happened in France.

Yet *Le Monde*'s initial assessment of news values was in a sense appropriate. For the English, the storm was an instant epic. Our backs were to the wall: the bulldog spirit was called for, and we were not found wanting: we knew what we owed to ourselves. But the French temperament is not disposed to find anything especially inspiring about getting in the way of an unforeseen external calamity: heroism is only heroic in France if it involves a deliberate and preferably gratuitous challenge to the elements, or some other testing circumstance.

Here, on the other hand, it is hardly good form to go out looking for trouble. It is better to rise doggedly to the occasion when afflicted by some disaster that one has done nothing at all to provoke. It is scarcely even a drawback if there has been a failure to guard against the possibility by taking reasonable precautions.

Le Monde's London correspondent referred back felicitously to the Blitz, in tune with our own ubiquitous invocations of the Dunkirk spirit and the Falklands. For us, if the weathermen had slipped up, that was an only-to-be-expected part of the familiar pattern of events. There could have been no Dunkirk if it had not been for the Men of Munich, no Falklands victory if the Foreign Office had not landed us in the soup, no hurricane heroism – or none so sweet – if Bracknell had got it right.

As for the Bretons, they had merely had a deeply unpleasant night, and were now faced with a huge and expensive mess to clear up. The stereotypes regarding the French peasantry are as well-established as the stereotypes enshrined in Ealing comedy: from Flaubert to Claude Berri's film *Jean de Florette* it is understood that the French peasant is narrow, short-sighted and deeply reluctant to raise a finger to help a neighbour in trouble. No perceptible prospect of good copy for the Parisian reader there.

In addition, Brittany is one of those places where tempests are expected to happen. It is hardened and on its guard, with the fragile corners already knocked off it, in a way that Cornwall or Caithness are on this side of the Channel. Its rocky headlands and low hills regularly endure the first rage of the autumn and winter storms which brew in Biscay. The outpost island of Ushant is one of the windiest places in the whole of Europe – and mild, too, under the flow of warm air brought spinning northwards by the passing depressions.

Brittany has its famous forests, such as Cranou, with its 300-year-old oaks, Fougères, a beech forest, once a centre for the manufacture of wooden sabots, and Paimpont, an ancient forest much depleted by iron-smelting in the Middle Ages, but partly replanted with pines. But they are open, heathy, forests for the most part, or modern commercial plantations. France is a deeply-wooded country – forest covers 23 per cent of its land area. But only 10 per cent of Brittany is wooded – a proportion similar to Britain's.

Brittany has great houses, too, but they tend to be *châteaux forts*, strongholds with massive battlements, as well-adapted to resisting the assaults of the wind as those of bandits and corsairs. The river Loire, which meets the sea at St Nazaire, flows past some of the most fragile and exquisite *châteaux* in the world, carved out of a pale stone which is the nearest architectural equivalent of ivory. But they are far upstream, 200 miles from the sea.

While the storm was gathering in Biscay, the British yacht *Island Endeavour* was crossing the bay on a passage from Salcombe to Madeira. The seasonal winds make autumn the most favourable time for yachtsmen taking the classic route from Europe towards the south. But Richard Baylay, her skipper, had had nothing but bad weather since setting out four days before. The boat was due to pick up equipment in La Rochelle, where it had been built, so he was obliged to head into the notorious bay instead of skirting round it.

On Thursday morning they were about 40 miles south of Brittany, making slow progress against a wind already blowing Force Nine, a "strong gale" of 45–50 mph: about the strongest wind a well-found yacht can hope to make headway against.

"When we were 40 miles south of Belle Ile, our mainsail ripped as we were reefing it, and I decided to turn back", says Baylay. "We ran before the wind under headsail alone for four hours, with large waves coming up behind us – with wet shirt-tails, as they say. It was lucky I knew Belle Ile well, because things were so wet that we couldn't have used a chart.

"We got into harbour at about lunchtime. Our radio forecast gave no warning of anything special, but the French told us that their television was giving out hurricane warnings. The ferryboat left harbour, because they were afraid the storm might be so strong that it would break its mooring lines and go adrift.

"At seven at night, the electricity failed, over the whole island. We were lying quite snugly, but on the other side of the harbour we could see the fishermen struggling in the light of car headlamps to stop their boats being damaged, as the wind thrust them against the quay. The inflatable fenders between the boats and the quay were going pop, and they were fetching car tyres to put down in their place.

"Our mate went off to look round, and he came back saying that he'd seen ambulances and fire engines rushing to and fro, and that chimneys had started crashing down around him.

"Believe it or not, we went to bed, and actually got some sleep with the wind blowing Force Twelve overhead. In the morning we hired a car and drove round the island. There was damage everywhere, and hardly a tree left standing – trees hundreds of years old just lying on their sides. The power was off most of the day. But people didn't seem too perturbed. They are used to fairly bad weather there."

"It was an experience I'm very glad to have had – but at the time I could very well have done without it."

The stoic attitude that Richard Baylay noted may have been typical. The Bretons are used to gales, though not on the scale of this one. Fifty miles west of Belle Ile is Concarneau. It is a crowded harbour, rather exposed to south-west winds. The pontoons of the floating marina were battered to pieces and 250 boats were set adrift. As the pontoons began to break up, firemen ran round the swaying walkways ordering sleeping yachtsmen to get off their boats fast. There was no time to extricate the boats from the tangle of hawsers and collapsing gangways, or even to retrieve more than a few handfuls of equipment. The state of the sea outside the harbour, dotted with rocks and now white with the low-lying mist of airborne foam that denotes a killing tempest, prohibited escape to open water.

A hundred and fifty boats were thrown in heaps "like mere shingle" against the ramparts of the old fortress, and battered to pieces. Thousands of pounds' worth of damage was done. "There was nothing we could do", M. Folgoas, Secretary to the *Mairie*, told *Le Monde* afterwards. "The force of the wind was more than anything we had ever seen before."

At Guilvenec, 20 miles west of Concarneau, a hundred boats were sheltering, including fishing boats which had hurried home on hearing the storm warnings. Six trawlers were damaged when they were thrown against the sea walls, and two others were driven ashore. But Guilvenec counted itself lucky. The losses would have been greater if the storm had not come on a day when the rise and fall of the tide was smaller than on almost any other day of the year. A tiny inlet of sand with rocky banks, it is sheltered by outlying reefs. Even at high water on October 15, these protective barriers stood higher out of the water than usual, and broke much of the force of the savage waves driving in out of the darkness.

The same providential factor prevented untold damage and possible loss of life all round the Breton coast, and for hundreds of miles beyond. In and around the busy port of Lorient, midway between Belle Ile and Concarneau, about 50 yachts and fishing boats were torn from their moorings and drifted away. At Port-la-Forêt, 700 pleasure boats were laid up afloat for the winter in a large marina with 30 pontoons. Ten of the pontoons gave way under the battering of the waves, and empty boats were tossed against each other: dozens were "cracked open like nuts".

The great marina at Cherbourg, which the *Malcolm Miller* had sailed past so peacefully a few hours before, was devastated. Cherbourg faces north, and not so much as a ripple can roll into its harbour past the monumental granite defences that Napoleon built there, using the labour of captured prisoners. The town is surrounded by rocky crags crowned with innumerable forts, relics of a long chapter of warfare stretching from Napoleon's day to Hitler's. Channelled between these hills, the wind attacked Cherbourg from behind, and laid waste to a floating village of yachts, unsuspectingly at rest in what is normally one of the securest places of refuge in the entire English Channel.

The damage inland was more extensive still, and far more serious in economic terms. Fishing is Brittany's largest industry, but thanks to low tides and advance warnings the damage it suffered was lighter than might have been feared. Tourism is the next largest, with yachting an important part of it: the loss in vessels and facilities was severe. But agriculture and forestry, which make up the third most important industry, suffered worst of all.

A century ago the small farmers of north-western France had a manner of life which was arduous, slow to change and necessarily self-reliant. It had to be so when the market town might be hours away, and when there were no tractors and no pylon lines bringing power to be tapped at will. Today an agriculture has evolved which is as unlike that of the past as it could possibly be. European Community grants have brought into being an industry as productive and diverse as anywhere in France, but as dependent on external resources and communications as it is on grants..

On a normal day, Brittany's roads are full of lorries carrying ripe lettuce and tomatoes to the processing plant, eggs to the packager and hens to their final appointment with the electric stunning machine. Many farmers had invested in plant to do much of the work of processing their produce themselves, and had organised into local cooperatives to do so.

It is a system with elements of the grotesque at the best of times, as it churns out vast quantities of beef, milk and butter far in excess of the needs of Europe or any other market able to pay a full price for it. It never looked more grotesque than it did that night. The artificiality and fragility of the system were exposed as starkly as the stalls and pens inside the farm buildings whose roofs the tempest peeled away.

On this sophisticated husbandry the storm came down as hungrily as a swarm of locusts. Standing crops, dairy farms, veal batteries, greenhouses, vineyards and plantations were all battered by the onslaught. It rose to its full force at about ten at night, and blew for four hours. Even inland, it reached speeds as high as 125 mph. Wooden barns and farmhouses were shaken until their timbers groaned aloud. Tiles, slates and sharp-edged sheets of corrugated iron were torn from their places and sent flying through the darkness. Cars and lorries were overturned, house roofs stripped open, and the indispensible pylon lines torn down.

Some farmers ventured out to try to secure barns or hen-houses which seemed about to collapse. But most of those who tried soon came in again, for fear of the flying debris.

Le Monde described in belated reports how the market gardener Joseph Coathalen and his wife struggled for two hours to save their 16,000 square feet of greenhouses. They enjoyed some shelter from a bank planted with oaks and poplars. The two of them did their best to tie down the shaking buildings with ropes. But at midnight the windbreak of trees was swept away at a stroke, and within ten minutes the greenhouses lay in ruins.

Hundreds of cattle, pigs and poultry scattered terrified far and wide over the countryside, after their dwellings had been shaken to pieces over their heads. Over an area of 80,000 hectares, or nearly 200,000 acres, fields of maize destined for winter feed and almost ready for harvesting were beaten to the ground.

But the worst damage of all was borne by the trees, in France as in Britain a few hours later. In a diagonal band 20 to 25 miles wide, running right across the Breton peninsula from Quimper in the south to Pontorson in the north, within sight of Mont St Michel, the land was virtually cleared of trees. Four days after the catastrophe, the *Coopérative des sylviculteurs bretons* estimated that between three-quarters and one-third of the province's forest acreage had been damaged to a significant extent, and predicted that overall losses might reach *"deux ou trois milliards de francs de pertes"*, the equivalent of £300 million.

"This wipes out 30 years of effort by thousands of owners, aided by the national forestry fund", said M. Tanguy de Kernier, President of the Co-operative, whose 2,000 members include many small farmers ill-prepared to bear a setback on such a scale.

The magnificent beech forests of Normandy, like Lyons-la-Forêt near Rouen, seem to have suffered less catastrophic damage than their English counterparts. But the overall loss to French forestry was staggering: the total volume of timber brought down was seven million cubic metres, almost twice the English total. But France is so much richer in its forests than Britain that the relative loss – and the psychological impact – were smaller. A storm in 1982 had brought down no less than 12 million cubic metres.

Towns suffered as well as the countryside. In Quimper, part of the roof of the police headquarters disappeared. In Morlaix, on the opposite coast of Brittany, the roof of a supermarket flew away "as if it were paper". In the city of Caen, 180 miles downwind in Normandy, a belfry turret crashed down from the *Abbaye des Hommes*, the great Romanesque church founded by William the Conqueror as a worthy place for his bones to rest. The abbey has three spires, two medieval and one modern, but the belfry that collapsed seems to have been only a minor part of the structure, though it crushed four cars parked beneath.

Ten other cars were buried in a small avalanche further north, in the Département of Seine-Maritime, beyond Le Havre. The cars were parked under a hillside which collapsed and brought 30 tons of rock down onto them. In three areas of the Channel coast alone, the fire brigade answered 5,300 emergency calls in 18 hours. The gale was felt as far away as Paris, where a giant crane being used to build an arch in the modern suburb of La Défense collapsed and blocked a main road into Paris throughout the morning rush hour.

Many of those who spent the night awake in the din of breaking windows and falling tiles commented on the unnatural warmth that the storm brought. Some called it stifling; some looked at their thermometers and saw that they stood at no less than 30°C (85° Fahrenheit) – as mild as a sunny summer's day.

Then, quite suddenly, it was all over. A hush fell which was almost uncanny after the hours of deafening noise. And with the hush began to come appreciation of the scale of the disaster. First reports suggested that the advance warnings had succeeded in preventing any deaths. But it seems that there were at least two. Near Quimper, a civil servant was reported to have been crushed to death by a tree. A cyclist at St Aubin-les-Elbeuf, near Rouen, was killed when a gust flung him against a roadside pylon. And a nine-year-old girl in St Malo was seriously hurt when the chimney of her house collapsed into her bedroom.

In the towns there was the damage from fallen masonry and hoardings to clear up. Major centres like Quimper, Paimpol, Concarneau and Lorient were completely without power. Dozens of telephone exchanges were out of action.

In the country there was a virtually total breach in communications. Roads everywhere were blocked with a welter of broken branches, and hundreds of miles of power and telephone lines were down. Although there was not much damage to the main arteries of the electrical supply system it was obvious that its veins and capillaries stretching to the more isolated hamlets would take many days to restore.

It was a devastating blow to the most intensely farmed territory in the whole of France. Farming – even high-tech factory farming – is not like industrial manufacture, where it is relatively simple to close the plant down if power or supplies are interrupted. If the highly integrated machine of modern agriculture is disrupted, its operatives are left not with idle production lines, but with millions of living animals needing to be fed and tended, and acres of produce incessantly continuing to ripe and ripe, or rot and rot.

Cut off the supply lines and it rapidly becomes a struggle to feed livestock. Cut off the road to the abbatoir, and animals marked down for slaughter have to be given a reprieve, eating their heads off and blessing their stars for the hurricane. Cut off the electricity, and the whole elaborate system for machine-feeding of mass-produced poultry, pigs and calves suddenly becomes useless. Cows queue up, waiting uncomfortably to be milked, and a workforce tailored to the labour-saving routines of mechanical milking are forced to set about milking them by hand. Cut off the water pumps, and livestock begin to die and produce starts to shrivel within a matter of hours.

It was necessary to make shift with bucket and shovel to keep the basic work going. In some respects, factory farming implies a degree of luxury. Breeding sows were accustomed to lying in centrally heated sheds, row upon row of billowing mothers, with their naked babies struggling to reach their many teats. When the power failed, the newborn piglets began to die of cold. Calves being fattened up for veal were accustomed to a diet of warm milk, and refused to drink when faced with cold milk.

The problems of milking did not end with the job itself, which in many farms went on all night by the dim light of oil lamps. Blocked roads disrupted the collection system, and left farmers with thousands of gallons which had to be thrown away because they could not be stored. Community regulations lay down strict standards for the storage of milk, which can only be met with electric equipment. The failure of electric cooling systems meant that much of the milk collected with so much labour was impossible to sell legally.

Arable farmers started a hue and cry for harvesters. It was essential to beg or borrow equipment to harvest the ruined maize crop. If the crop was not brought under cover within hours, it would rot where it lay, if rain followed the gale, which it soon did. It was hard even to contact farmers in unaffected areas who might have harvesters to hire, and harder still to get them to the spot along roads blocked by trees every few hundred yards.

The French have had a kind of love affair with electricity in recent years. The country is not well-endowed with its own sources of energy, and the authorities have sought to escape the political dangers of over-dependence on outside sources by embarking on a gigantic nuclear power programme. In the process, they have invested electricity with a glamour which our own Central Electricity Generating Board has never managed to generate. It is a thing to boast of to be 'all-electric': clean, modern, with an overtone of the patriotic. Demand has grown so much that the supply network is apt to become overburdened. British farmers and householders a few hours later found themselves facing many of the same problems as the French, but they were measurably less dependent on the power which had come down the now useless lines.

Inside the home,the power cut victims had to cope with all the obvious everyday deprivations of light, heat, television, cooking and refrigeration. Many had deep-freezes filled with hundreds of pounds' worth of stored food – not to mention trophies of the hunt – which would rapidly spoil if they thawed out. In some cases, they were loaded aboard trucks and left with relatives outside the stricken area. In some villages, they were assembled at the *Mairie* and laid out in rows in the reception room, like coffins from some disaster more costly in human life, so that one generator could keep the chill off for all of them.

Since the French do not share our own national aversion to fresh bread, bakery manufacture is much more dispersed than it is here. Instead of a fleet of vans delivering bread wrapped, sliced, yielding and inoffensive to every village store, every village has its own bakery, equipped with the latest thing in electric ovens. It became a battle simply to get hold of a loaf. In some districts, families were rationed to one loaf (*"boule"*) a day. Some people drove 20 miles to join long queues outside bakeries which did not have to ration their output.

Many of the mobile generators which had suddenly become worth their weight in gold began a shuttle from bakery to bakery down whichever roads were passable, allowing each one to raise the fires for one hasty baking. Others were taken from farm to farm, working day and night to give each of them a boost and allow minimal activity to be carried on. In Coray in Finisterre, a 37-year-old carpenter called Jean Ollu let his business go hang, said *Le Monde*, while he drove between farms towing a generator behind his van. He carried on for a week, working from dawn to nightfall, and refused to accept a penny in payment. Spontaneously, neighbour began to help neighbour, and district to ask how it could give aid to district.

Six *départements* were plunged into a new life, or a new-old life reminiscent of 50 years ago. It took the rest of France a little while to wake up the the scale of the disaster, because Paris had not been seriously affected, and the metropolitan opinion-makers did not wake on Friday morning to find catastrophe unmistakeably spread before their eyes (as did the media-people of Blackheath and Kew). It was not until more than a week after the storm that a specially convened council of ministers declared the six regions an official disaster area.

But as the authorities began to dispatch armies of repairmen to restore communications, and farm collectives in other parts of the country began to respond to appeals for assistance, the wider public started to become aware of the strange time warp that the villagers of Brittany and Normandy had been swept into – and also to realise that prodigies of improvisation, self-sufficiency and mutual aid were being accomplished there. The British began to blow fanfares to the heroism of their own storm-fighters almost before the wind had dropped; the French only slowly noticed that there were fanfares to be blown on their side of the Channel too.

In the sudden hush of the dawn after the storm, its victims noticed that there was no birdsong outside, and scarcely a sign of a bird. Had they been carried away out to sea, or buried under tons of shattered foliage ? And the Bretons noticed with wonder that the leaves everywhere – those which remained on the trees as well as those torn away – had been turned almost black in a single night. The day before, they had scarcely begun to lose their summer tint; now they were shrivelled and darkened by an ugly affliction quite unlike the natural changes brought by autumn.

They had been poisoned by salt. The wind had come off the sea with such force that it had carried salt spray with it 20 or 30 miles inland, spreading in one night a scorching desolation everywhere it touched, like one of the plagues of Egypt.

CHAPTER 4

ACROSS THE ISLANDS

"From Ushant to Scilly is thirty-five leagues."
(Sea Chanty: anon; perhaps 1620s)

Nobody would take the trouble, as Arthur Ransome's Peter Duck once observed, to measure such an out-of-the-way course as the distance from Ushant to Scilly – let alone make a song about it – unless they had been in a sailing ship working its way with effort and weariness up the English Channel against a foul wind, on the final stages of a homeward voyage.

Ushant is the great landfall for all sea travellers to northern Europe from the worlds of the south and the east. On passing it, in the age of sail, they were faced with one last sea wilderness, in which a vessel could zigzag for days on end from headland to treacherous headland, before it could find its way safely past "Plymouth, Start, Portland and Wight", and home to London, Hamburg or Rotterdam.

Today the Channel is a highway marked out, signposted and policed as effectively as any motorway, with eastbound and westbound lanes imposed on its shifting waters and ratified by international agreement. Vessels which stray out of the correct lane can be fined like jay-walkers, and millions of tons of shipping drive up it every day as straightforwardly as if it was a canal. It is laid out to plain view even in the thickest weather on radar screens on the bridges of vessels powerful enough to disregard almost any extreme of weather. It seems to have no secrets or surprises left.

But on the night of October 15, the Channel became once again what it always was. As the gale flowed across it from France towards a sleeping England, the sea was whipped up into a wilderness in which mariners had to fight for their ships and their lives, caught as much by surprise by the change in the weather as their forebears must often have been. Any vessel on the move that night was in danger, and even large vessels safe in harbour were torn from their moorings and sent careering downwind like cockleshells. The worst stress and damage was suffered not by small boats, nor even by the few remaining sailing ships, like the *Malcolm Miller,* with her crew of youngsters who had scarcely been to sea before – but by cargo ships, cross-Channel ferries and oil-rig ships with seasoned crews used to operating in the narrow seas in all seasons and weathers.

It will never be possible to say with certainty where the gale of 1987 stands in the long list of Channel storms recorded through history. Records allow some comparisons to be made with the storm of 1953, which rolled up a killing tide that flooded across much of East Anglia, and even with the north-easter of 1893 which took more than 300 lives at sea alone. In the *Royal Charter* gale of 1859, 454 lives were lost in a single shipwreck. But the information does not exist to allow statistical comparisons with the legendary tempest of 1703, chronicled in detail by Daniel Defoe, the author of *Robinson Crusoe*, or with the gales of 1665 and 1666 mentioned by Pepys in his diary – let alone with the portentous gale which raged across England on the night Oliver Cromwell died.

The barometer is said to have fallen lower than its 1987 level in 1665 and again in 1821, in London at least. The former reading is regarded with scepticism today, for no precise records could be made in those days. The week-long gale of 1703 is generally thought of as the worst of all, because of its long duration and the astonishingly high number of recorded casualties – it caused 8,000 deaths by land and sea.

Some of these storms have a life of their own in legend and literature. Cromwell's storm inspired Samuel Butler to declare in the doggerel of *Hudibras* that "Tossed in a raging hurricane Did Oliver give up his reign". The more sophisticated Edmund Waller – so sophisticated that he ran off a doleful lament for Cromwell and then a joyful welcome for Charles II the moment the political wind changed – turned the same event into a cosmic hyperbole:

> "His dying groans, his last breath, shake our isle,
> And trees uncut fall for his funeral pile. . ."

The storm of 1703 has a special immortality because it was recorded by the industrious Defoe in a superb piece of extended pot-boiling journalism entitled, in an exuberance of typography: *THE STORM or, a collection of the most Remarkable CASUALTIES AND DISASTERS which happen'd in the Late Dreadful TEMPEST, both by SEA AND LAND.*

Defoe had been put in the pillory and sent to Newgate not long before, for writing a political pamphlet which had displeased the government. Released, with a wife and six children to support, he was in desperate need of a non-political commercial subject. The storm must have seemed providential to him. He simply put an advertisement into the paper and found – as I did – that people were only too pleased to tell their stories. He added a commentary which is a masterpiece of dramatic, scrupulous and circumstantial reporting, and sent the lot off to the printers – spontaneous recall as it came to hand, pious, pompous, simple or halting.

Reading this collection of undiluted first-hand testimony in the light of the events of 1987, one repeatedly finds that one's skin tingles with a sense ‚of recognition: physical details and human reactions correspond with an uncanny closeness. It is as if it was the same event re-enacted, and the same people. It would have been possible without strain to have found an appropriate line from *The Storm* to head every chapter of this book. Defoe deserved to make a fortune out of it: but the signs are that he did not.

In his narrative, the presiding role in the whole drama is assigned to the Almighty. "I cannot believe any Man so rooted in Atheistical Opinions as not to find some cause to doubt . . . and a little to apprehend the Possibility of a Supreme Being, when he felt the terrible Blasts of the Tempest", he says.

The wind as a phenomenon appeals equally to his religious and his scientific imagination. "There seems to be more of God in the whole Appearance, than in any other part of Operating Nature . . . As the Storm was first felt from the West, some have conjectur'd that the first Generation or rather Collection of Materials, was from the Continent of America, possibly from that part of Florida and Virginia where, if we respect natural Causes, the Confluence of Vapours raised by the Sun . . . might afford sufficient Matter for the Exhalation. I am the rather inclined to this opinion because we are told, they felt upon that Coast an unusual Tempest a few days before . . . We may suppose a Conjunction of some confederate Matter, which might fall in with it by the way . . ."

Floyd and Biscay, in a nutshell.

The most notorious victim of the 1703 gale – almost, one feels, its Faustian impresario – was Henry Winstanley. He was an entrepreneur of great persistence and phenomenal powers of persuasion, who conceived and accomplished a project which had until his time been thought utterly impossible. He resolved to build a lighthouse on the Eddystone Rock, a tooth of red granite which lies ten miles from land just in the path of ships sailing to or from Plymouth.

Winstanley had endless struggles to bed foundations in the hard rock, and on one occasion his workforce was seized by an enemy fleet and carried away to France. But he convinced the French that his project was for the good of humanity as a whole, and persuaded his backers at home to keep up the supply of funds. At last, in 1699, his masterpiece was completed.

Modern eyes are used to those graceful and functional tapering light-houses, built of masonry knitted together with dovetail joints, which are the descendants of the lighthouse built on the Eddystone more than a century afterwards by John Smeaton (a shape suggested to him, it is said, by the weather resistance of "the pyramidical shape of an aged oak"). By comparison, Winstanley's four-sided timber tower embellished with everything that was most frivolous in the way of galleries and pinnacles looks like a gesture of mere impertinence. But the world was impressed, and Winstanley declared that his confidence in his lighthouse was so complete that he wished he could be in it in the greatest storm that ever blew.

His wish was granted. And of course, when the storm of 1703 finally died down, not a trace of him or his lighthouse was to be seen. In its way, it was rather a splendid way to go, and wholly in character. Defoe does not fail to mention that a model of the lighthouse in Winstanley's house near Saffron Walden was smashed by the wind in the same night.

But when the gale of 1987 shook today's Eddystone light, there was not a soul aboard to listen to the waves thumping against the walls, or to wonder if this might be the storm that would at last find it wanting. The Elders of Trinity House have pursued a policy in recent years – undoubtedly economical and arguably humane – of converting their offshore lighthouses to automatic operation, so that their lights can be worked by remote control, with no more than a visit for maintenance every six months.

To judge by Jim Bowling, its crew would have taken things pretty much in their stride anyway. He served four and a half years on the Eddystone before being transferred to his present less arduous billet, the North Foreland, which is a quarter of a mile from the sea and has a garden gate straight out onto the road. In Defoe's storm, the North Foreland light was a blazing beacon of coals, which set fire to thatched cottages for miles around with its scattered embers. But today it is a domesticated spot.

"One year is much the same as another on the Eddystone", Jim Bowling says. "We used to serve two months out there at a time, and a month off – weather permitting. Sometimes I did three and a half months at a time, in the days before they built a helipad above the lantern.

"When a gale blows, there is a terrific noise, especially up in the lantern, where the wind roars through the ventilator. The whole tower vibrates with every sea that hits it, and even the cups and saucers on the table shake. It is designed to do that because a structure with some flexibility can have more strength than a rigid one."

By chance, one lighthouse of the classic type was occupied that night. The Wolf Rock, 80 miles to the west of the Eddystone, was in the process of being converted to automatic operation. When sailors in the past made their long detour "from Ushant to Scilly" in the teeth of a persistent north-easter, it was the Wolf they looked for, to know that it was time to double back again.

Len Astley was one of the team doing the job, and was woken up in his bunk sometime in the small hours. "It was the movement of the tower that woke me," he says. "We don't need to keep watches, because there is a big automatic buoy beside us to keep the light going while the conversion is going on. There was green water coming halfway up the tower – it is 160 feet high – and spray was going right over the top. When the waves hit it, the tower gave a jerky motion, a shake.

"We hadn't been warned that things would be as bad as this, and so the brass storm doors that you can fit over the windows were open. Water just came gushing in, and went everywhere. The place is damp enough at the best of times. We have a gas heater, but the condensation inside is very bad. It was pretty scary. You couldn't help thinking about that 'once-in-a-hundred-years wave' that they talk about."

In fact the Eddystone was only on the fringe of what was to become the most intense area of disturbance, and the Wolf was almost 200 miles from it. The centre of the deepening hurricane-force depression passed almost exactly over the Eddystone at one in the morning, by British Summer Time.

Like the legendary point of calm at the centre of a tropical typhoon, the centre of the depression was a point of relative stillness, between the masses of fast-moving air lumbering off-target towards the low point of pressure which had provoked their motion.

The centre was drifting north-east at about thirty miles an hour, and warm air from the south was violently rushing in to collide tumultuously with the cold air lying inertly over England, all along a line which ran north-east as far as London, and then doubled back sharply to cross the French coast again. As that bulge expanded in the next few hours, the speed of the warm inflow would dramatically increase.

The Wolf was on the opposite side of the centre of the depression, and the 70-mph airstream pouring over it at midnight was cold air coming from the north, sucked down in the opposite direction to the humid gale which was at the same moment thrusting northward over France. Many witnesses noticed the sharp rise in temperature. In Wrotham, Kent, Trevor Bardell drove back to his rather smart home in his rather smart car at about 9.30pm, after a game of squash. "I said to my wife that it was extraordinarily warm, a most peculiar night."

It was not until midnight that the real force of the hot northward airflow had already arrived over the first point of British soil to feel its lash. The Iles Minquiers, 150 miles to the south and east of the Wolf, are a scatter of almost uninhabited rocks which mark the southernmost point of the Channel Islands. They are so close to Brittany that their ownership was disputed between England and France for centuries, until after the last war. The wind that fell on France fell next on the Channel Isles, and spread the same devastation there.

The Channel Islands are used to wind. It was claimed in the local press that before the night of the hurricane the strongest gust ever recorded in the islands in any October was one of 108 mph, measured in Jersey in 1964. Jersey lost that record in the night – along with much else of a breakable description – when a gust of 110 mph was recorded in Guernsey.

The damage was far worse than it had been in 1964, even though the strength of the wind was not very different. The wind in 1964 was from the west, as most of the biggest Channel Island gales are. All the trees that grow in the islands have to be deeply anchored against assault from that side, or they do not survive long. The 1987 gale came initially from the south, and caught the trees wrong-footed, so to speak. Then it veered towards the west and sought out any weak points that were to be found there. Some householders found that the tiles on their roofs had been rasped off on two different sides of the house.

By midnight, the fire engines and ambulances were already out in the islands. Trees were falling, roofs flying away into the air, live power cables fracturing, and alarm calls pouring in. Hundreds of parish officials and public works employees turned out in the night to help the emergency services rescue the trapped and injured.

The first casualties on British soil were probably fireman David Brindel and his colleague Bob Gallie. They were called out when a tree fell on a house in Clos des Sables, in Jersey, just after midnight. As they arrived, a second tree fell right on top of them. Chris Jennett, a part-time fireman, freed them from the tree, and they were taken to hospital. Bob Gallie had suffered severe bruising and torn ligaments in the leg, but he was allowed to go home after treatment. David Brindel was more seriously hurt, and was kept in hospital with a hairline fracture of the skull.

Midnight was the moment when everything started giving way. Drivers were trapped in their cars, two motorcyclists skidded on wet leaves and had to be taken to hospital, and several people were injured by flying debris. A joint operation by firemen and ambulancemen moved more than 60 people from their homes in Route Orange, west Jersey, because the houses were in danger from the splendid rank of pine trees which lined the avenue. The people were taken to spend the rest of the night at a local school.

The local authority had been gravely considering how to frame a publicly acceptable programme for the replacement of these trees, no longer in their first youth. It is the nemesis which eventually befalls any avenue, however majestic: whether to cut and replace by degrees or make a clean sweep. A gradual process had been considered essential here, but it was hard to decide which trees should be sacrificed first. Now the dilemma was solved as the majority were struck down in one night, and the survivors left with splintered scars, as if a bomb had exploded among them.

At the same place two hours after the evacuation, four members of the island's Honorary Police were nearly killed by a section of roof torn from a supermarket. They were directing sightseeing traffic away from the avenue, which was completely blocked, when they heard "an almighty crash". Centenier Barry Walsh, their leader, told the *Jersey Evening Post* next day: "Because of the wind we didn't hear it go. We didn't realise where it had come from or what it was. At the time, I thought: "What the hell is that ?" There were iron girders and large pieces of wood all over the place, and some of the smaller stuff was still being thrown around. I told the men to move out of the way."

Mr Walsh paid tribute to members of a visiting Territorial Army unit and to many members of the public who had turned out to give aid to victims. He had even seen one who had gone out on crutches to offer his help, he said. Because the storm arrived in the Channel Islands a few hours earlier than it did on the mainland, a larger number of people seem to have been out and about, for better or worse (on the mainland the storm was the catastrophe most of us slept through). This makes it all the more remarkable that there were no deaths. The Jersey hospital treated 11 people for significant injuries during the storm, including the two firemen.

More than 500 fallen trees were blocking the island's main roads, and it was impossible to guess how many lay across its minor ones. The difficulties in getting about to deal with the hundreds of emergency calls were almost insurmountable. One fire engine went to help a man trapped in a car which had been crushed under a tree, only to be hit by a falling tree itself. Before it could be extricated, another tree fell just behind it, preventing it from moving either forwards or back. Meanwhile the trapped man was released, but the fire engine remained trapped for hours afterwards. Elsewhere, a police car was immobilised in almost the same way.

Orders went out that fire engines operating away from their bases should not try to get back, but should stay to handle emergencies in the areas where they were.

In the centre of the main town of St Helier damage was mostly superficial, with some shop windows and canopies smashed, and about 35 trees toppled in the park. But some buildings were damaged spectacularly. A four-storey block in the Mayfair Hotel lost the whole of its flat roof, and three other hotels in the island were seriously damaged. Guests staying in the block were evacuated only a few minutes before the roof went. One guest staying on the top floor was Mr Desmond Jones, who is disabled. The night porter and another guest helped him downstairs just in time. "I was sound asleep when the fire alarm went off, and then I heard banging on the door", said Mr Jones. "The window blew in and curtains flew across the room. I'm really lucky to be alive."

Another flat roof which peeled away in the night was at Landfield Court, a block of flats in St Helier. One of the residents, Mrs Christine Keen, fled from the block early in the storm with her eight-month-old baby, and took refuge with a neighbour opposite. As the roof disintegrated, a large wooden plank flew right across the road and crashed through the window of the room where Mrs Keen and her baby were sitting, as if the storm was trying to hunt her down. She had to throw herself across the room to avoid it.

Occupants of the flats had heard their roof "flapping" in the wind. Mrs Sally Cornell got up to investigate the noises; "Ten minutes later, we were out. I grabbed my son and ran. My husband and a neighbour went back to see if there was anything that could be done, but there wasn't and about an hour later, the whole lot just took off. I've never been so frightened in the whole of my life."

"It seems a miracle no-one was killed" said Police Superintendant Bob Le Breton in the morning. There had been a time when they had sent out a request for helicopter support, fearing some disaster with serious casualties at a spot inaccessible on the blocked roads.

None of Jersey's schools opened next morning, and thousands of people trying to get to work found their way barred by fallen trees. A team of 130 men managed to re-open most of the main roads by Friday afternoon, but in most cases only to single-file traffic. It was days before power and telephone lines were fully restored.

The Torbay Seaways ferry *Devonian*, which had set sail for Torquay from Jersey on Thursday evening, was overtaken by the storm and turned back to shelter in Guernsey. But they could not dock in the 90-mph gusts, and spent the night in the channel between Guernsey and Herm. They did not tie up until 7 am on Friday, and the 123 passengers and 27 crew had an uncomfortable night. Two men were taken to hospital in St Peter Port with minor injuries, but were able to rejoin the ship before she sailed in the evening, after the passengers had been given a day ashore to recover. The ship's captain said that conditions had been some of the worst he had known. *Devonian* finally arrived at Torquay that night, 19 hours behind schedule.

In the Channel Islands, as in France, agriculture suffered severely. Like their Breton counterparts, dairy farmers were faced with the problem of herds needing to be milked, and no electric milking machinery. With some of the larger herds, it was impossible to milk all the cows by hand. Some farmers took their herds to neighbouring farms for milking. But the Jersey Electricity Company made milking sheds its top priority, and power was back on again almost everywhere before Friday was over. Being more compact, and having many of their power lines underground, the islands did not have quite the same communications problems as Brittany, where many farms were without power for days.

With their mild climate, the islands have gone into horticulture and greenhouse farming on a large scale, and the long-term damage in this sector was more serious than the effect on dairy farming. Those interminable tubular constructions which have replaced the glass glasshouse, and look like giant rolls of kitchen plastic wrapping, were particularly vulnerable to the wind. Many lay in ruins, with shreds of plastic tattered over the hedges far to leeward. Their flimsy metal frameworks had often collapsed as well, leaving the plants inside open to the elements. Insurance companies refuse to insure these shelters, and many farmers were faced with a total loss. (The things are cheap, though: one daffodil rearer lost 11 large tunnels, and put the loss at £7,000).

Outdoor crops like courgettes and tomatoes were wiped out, and tougher plants like cauliflower and calabrese suffered badly too. One grower of carnations and orchids lost 20 per cent of his glasshouses, and predicted on the morning after that his overall losses could be well over £100,000. It was clear at once that the losses for agriculture in Jersey alone would run into many millions.

But it was the loss of the trees that affected the islanders' imaginations most. With their exposure to winds, the islands have depended heavily on tree cover to provide shelter, and to shield the rapid recent growth in building from the eye of the tourist. A sense of nakedness was apparent, majestically expressed by a leading article in that week's *Jersey Weekly Post*.

"Jersey will never be the same again in the lifetime of anyone reading these words", it declared. Houses could be repaired, but the ravages to "thousands of trees, many great and aged" could not be fully restored until "today's children have their own great-great-grandchildren . . . It was, perhaps, the nearest to a holocaust the Island has come in recorded time".

Holocaust imagery was a relatively infrequent alternative to Dunkirk imagery in the distinctive rhetoric that the storm evoked over the wide swathe of Britain that it touched. It appeared unseemly to make comparisons between the destruction of inanimate vegetables, however beautiful and however much beloved, with the abominations of Belsen and Auschwitz. In the Channel Islands, the only part of Britain where the Nazis were actually in a position to impose their persecutions, the image rang particularly strangely.

But in the weeks following the storm, there must have been many in the damaged areas who found that the piles of truncated limbs, heaped up under the sky in great morgues of timber, reminded them irresistibly of those photographs of a worse, man-made, destruction which we can never forget.

CHAPTER 5

THE FIRST DEATHS

*"Hark! to those sounds! They're from distress at sea:
How quick they come! What terrors may there be!"*
(George Crabbe, *The Borough*)

As the little *Royalist* prudently "scuttled" into Weymouth at teatime on Thursday, to avoid the coming storm that the weathermen had failed to give warning of, she was passed by a spanking new ocean-going yacht on the way out – the catamaran *Sunbeam Chaser*, with a crew of seven, off to chase sunbeams in the West Indies.

The training ship tied up near where the Channel Island ferries unload, and put out extra mooring lines in case of trouble. The teenage cadets were sent to bed, and most of them slept soundly through all that was to come.

"Luckily we were pointing straight into the wind, so we were as comfortable as we could be", said David Norman, the *Royalist*'s sailing master. "It was getting very violent inside the harbour, and our wind speed indicator at the masthead was spinning faster and faster. The gauge hit the top at 65 knots, and stayed like that for three hours."

During the three hours between 4 am and 7 am, the barometer at Portland naval base rose by 25.4 millibars, the largest rise in pressure over a three-hour period ever recorded in the British Isles. At Hurn airport, near Bournemouth, the barometer rose 12.2 millibars in a single hour, which is not only an all-British record but a third as much again as the previous record, and an event statistically unlikely to recur for 500 years.

As the wind rose, an emergency call came through to the Weymouth lifeboat. Portland coastguards were concerned about the *Sunbeam Chaser*, making heavy weather of it 14 miles south-west of the headland. One of her crew was acutely seasick. Although it is unusual for a lifeboat to be launched for a ship which has not requested assistance, the decision was taken to go to the rescue.

All observers who saw the open Channel that night were struck by how extraordinarily quickly the sea got up. A large sea wave does not come into being without a good deal of grooming. Normally hundreds of miles of open water and the constant brusque manipulation of a steady wind are needed to tease many tons of water into standing up above the waterline and moving forward in ranks. It is a mark of the intense force of the storm that it generated in a very short time, and even in restricted waters, waves such as few had ever seen before.

Weymouth lies in the shelter of the great rock of Portland, which St Paul's Cathedral was once part of, until Sir Christopher Wren had it quarried out in blocks. Shelves of rock jut out under water into the Channel beyond the headland in such a way that the tidal flow tumbles over them like rapids in a stream, causing a tumult of water which can be uncomfortable, and dangerous, even in the calmest weather. The effect of wind and tide-race combined must have been nightmarish that night, and the lifeboat made slow progress against the gale on its way out to the catamaran's reported position.

The destroyer HMS *Birmingham*, sister ship to the *Sheffield* and *Coventry*, lost in the Falkland Islands, had also responded to the emergency call, and had stationed herself between the wind and the boat, protecting her from the worst of the weather and performing the proverbial function of spreading oil on troubled waters.

When the lifeboat eventually arrived, Derek Sargent, the coxwain, manoeuvred her alongside the *Sunbeam Chaser*. A small farce was then enacted among mountainous seas. The seven-man crew of the lifeboat signalled to the catamaran's crew to jump for it. Five men and a girl did so, but Derek Goverd, the skipper, stayed behind.

"I was amazed", said Mr Goverd afterwards. "I only expected one person who was seasick to leave. But they all got off, leaving me on my own. It was mutiny. I didn't think we needed to be rescued. The boat was dry, and is very strong. We were in no danger of running aground."

He insisted on steering his boat back towards Weymouth, to the irritation of the lifeboatmen, who were kept at sea two hours longer than they need have been, watching over his slow progress.

"We couldn't leave the man out there to die – that's not our style", said the lifeboat secretary, Lieutenant Commander Barney Morris, who had authorised the lifeboat's launch. "While there's a man on board a boat in trouble we have to stay on the scene. He behaved like an arrogant bastard. He put the lives of his own crew and my men at risk."

Coastguards were critical of Mr Goverd for sailing despite gale warnings which they had been putting out from twelve hours before the storm. He replied that the regular radio forecasts had not given a gale warning until hours after he had left port. The lifeboat was reported to have suffered minor structural damage, while the *Sunbeam Chaser* had suffered little more serious harm than torn sails. Mr Goverd was not a popular man on the Weymouth waterfront for a little while afterwards; but he had managed to save his ship.

As day broke, another yacht limped into Weymouth and tied up a few yards ahead of the *Royalist*. This was a smaller cruising boat which had broken from its moorings in the more exposed neighbouring anchorage of Portland, and had drifted helplessly across the harbour before fetching up against a sea wall, whence the Navy had rescued it.

The yacht was half swamped and gravely damaged. According to local rumour it had drifted in the night across the enclosures of a fish farm, and released some 30,000 young salmon to unexpected freedom. It is pleasant to speculate that some of these fry may safely complete their apprenticeship of migrations to the Sargasso Sea and back, and may reappear like their wild cousins in the waters in which they were born. Eventually that one night's mishap might turn Weymouth's inconsiderable estuary into one of the country's great salmon rivers.

Tales of damage and emergency could be told in most of the many creeks and anchorages between Weymouth and the Wash. The fiercest gales usually strike later in the season, when small boats have been safely laid up. In mid-October there were still hundreds afloat, in Poole, Yarmouth, Cowes, Chichester and many other havens – to be tossed around, thrown against one another, and swamped. Even yachts which had been taken out of the water were not wholly safe: in Bembridge, where thousands of pounds' worth of damage was done to boats, pontoons and shipyard buildings, many yachts propped up on timbers for the winter were blown over, shattering their planking as they fell.

.Not far from Bembridge, the *Malcolm Miller*, safely arrived from Cherbourg, had anchored off Cowes. A rather unexpected small boat bobbed alongside her. Coming up the Solent in the dusk, the schooner's crew had heard shouts, and found a little dinghy drifting with a lad aboard. His outboard motor had failed while he was trying to cross from the mainland to the island. It is significant that even though it was blowing almost a gale outside, the Solent was still calm enough for someone to get away with such municipal-pond antics.

Rather reluctantly, the *Miller* gave their surprise guest a berth for the night. The Customs were coming aboard in the morning to give the ship clearance, and did not want people slipping on and off her until then.

The 9 pm weather forecast predicted more moderate winds than they had had that day. Captain Adrian Allenby, the schooner's master, turned in at about 11 pm, with the usual "Call me if necessary" message to the watch.

"About one in the morning the watch officer came to tell me the wind was gusting to thirty knots, but that we were quite safe. Soon afterwards, the navigator, an experienced seaman, told me that it was gusting forty knots and that our anchor was beginning to drag. By the time I got to the bridge, it was fifty knots.

"I had never ever before had the ship dragging with that anchor, which is a heavy one – and we once rode out fifty knots of wind for several days with it. We put out more cable and a second anchor, and I got both engines going half ahead to stop us dragging further.

"I have been to the Antarctic and across Drake's Passage down there, and quite honestly, I hadn't seen a sea like that before. There was only half a mile between us and the shore for the waves to get up in, but it was enough to make us roll and pitch heavily, and for spray to come over the bridge, which it normally doesn't do, even at sea. It was jolly difficult even to look at the water because there was so much spray, and the wind in the rigging was making a high shriek which was deafening – absolutely horrendous. Every now and then it would seem to go quiet and the engineer would say 'It's dropping' – and then it would come back as strong as ever."

Captain Allenby considered waking the 37 trainees, between 16 and 24 years old, and bringing them on deck, ready for a quick evacuation in case the ship drifted onto the Hampshire shore, only about three miles away.

"If the anchor had failed in those seas, I don't think we could have kept her head to the wind, even with the engines. In that case . . . I don't know which is safer . . . one would just hope to blow aground somewhere one could get to the shore. But I decided to leave the crew in their bunks, and just bring one watch up at a time. This was partly to give the impression that things were not too out of the ordinary. They reacted very well, and one or two slept right through it.

"We lost the little dinghy – I was of a mind to cast it off in case it did some damage, but it solved that problem by swamping and breaking adrift. It was a newish boat, with a nice outboard, too. Some of our furled sails started coming out of the ties. It wasn't that they had been badly stowed – it was the sheer force of the wind. We knew they'd be damaged, but one couldn't go near them: a flying pulley-block can give you a nasty knock. We just had to leave them flogging to pieces.

"In the dark it was difficult to see any ropes coming adrift, and inevitably one that did happened to be near the starboard propellor and wrapped itself round the screw. Luckily that did not happen until the wind was decreasing, and we were able to hold the ship with only one engine.

"It was an interesting night. We were very lucky. Our sister ship, the *Sir Winston Churchill*, was tied up in Portsmouth all this time. I think we had a more comfortable time than they did, though potentially more hazardous. They were sideways on to the wind, and it heeled them to an angle of 20 degrees, even with no sails up.

"We kept noticing what we thought were terrific flashes of lightning everywhere. Then it dawned on us that it was too low down for lightning. It was electric cables carrying away, all over the Isle of Wight and along the other shore to Portsmouth."

A few miles away in Southampton, the 400-ton tanker *Barrier* broke from her moorings and nearly went aground, while at Hamble, almost within sight of the *Miller*, the 1,400-ton *Sam G* dragged her anchor and ended up on the mud. More serious maritime emergencies were to arise later in the night. But the havoc at sea was nothing to the havoc that was now beginning to break out on land.

To the east of a line slanting up north eastwards from Weymouth, the wind fell on the English coast at 2 am in an unparalleled onslaught. There was damage in the West Country as well, mainly in the form of flooding after heavy rain made its already brimming rivers overflow. Power cables were brought down, and as many as 4,000 homes across Devon and Cornwall were without electricity for part of the next day. But it was over east Dorset and the counties further east that the gale burst with full ferocity.

Across the Isle of Purbeck and the New Forest, the blast generated by Hurricane Floyd 4,000 miles away brought Britain an unaccustomed inkling of the kind of forces that a tropical storm can wield. Cables came down in showers of short-circuiting sparks. Tiles flew from roofs: sometimes the roofs followed them. Caravans were toppled like packing-cases. And everywhere the trees were coming down, smashing buildings, blocking roads and railways and uprooting telephone poles. Thousands of households were suddenly thrown back into a condition of isolation unknown in Wessex for a generation at least.

More than 25,000 homes in Dorset were left with little or no power, and thousands were also left without water, as power cuts stopped the machinery in at least 30 water and sewage pumping stations. Council workers in Wareham and many other places were out from the small hours onwards in response to emergency calls. At the police station at Lymington, Hampshire, where an officer later described the town as being in "complete chaos", more than 150 telephone calls reporting damage were recorded in a single hour.

In Swanage, Dorset, a party of 72 schoolchildren were hastily moved out of a caravan site and brought down into the safety of the town.

"The caravans started to move, so we evacuated", their teacher Paul Kaczmarek told the *Bournemouth Evening Echo* next day. "As we were getting the kids out, one unoccupied van turned over, so we got out very quickly. I've been up there today and one of the caravans occupied by six lads has been rolled up like a Swiss roll."

One of the areas to suffer most was the stretch of coast between Bournemouth – that tranquil haven of the retired – and the Solent. A line of low sandstone cliffs standing in the way of the airstream broke its flow into an especially destructive turmoil, a phenomenon which was to happen elsewhere that night. Miss Helen Barry, a 71-year-old living in a block of flats in Southbourne, Bournemouth, sat for much of the night on the edge of her bed wearing her wellington boots, hat and raincoat, and clutching her suitcase. "When the roof started moving I thought I would never see daylight, and would be buried alive under a pile of rubble", she told the local paper.

Alfred and Winifred Hazel, pensioners living in the same block as Miss Barry, ran to escape as their roof began to break up. If they had slept on they would have been killed.

"Within minutes of us getting up, a 15-foot roof beam landed on our bed", said Mr Hazel.

In Highcliffe, on the same line of cliffs, several other blocks of old people's flats, with hundreds of occupants, were partially evacuated as their roofs began to come away. Many tenants stayed put, but about 90 were taken to the local community centre.

"I suddenly saw the roof going up and down", said 90-year-old Mrs Iris

Grant. "I got dressed and went downstairs to a friend's flat. They would not let me up again."

Mrs Violet Pilley, aged 87, woke up at about 2 am and found found bits of plaster from the ceiling in her hair. "I did not know what to do but I thought I would make a cup of tea", she told a reporter. But the next thing she remembered was lying among debris on her kitchen floor, with a cut hand. The door had jammed, and she could not push it open.

"I sat there shivering with cold and thought I would never get out. Pieces kept falling down."

Meanwhile her friend Mrs Millicent Nicholson, who is 76, had also been woken up. She thought she must be dreaming when she saw the ceiling coming apart from the walls, until a gush of cold air and the sound of splintering wood told her that this was no dream. She struggled along the landing to see whether Mrs Pilley was all right and heard her calls for help. "I pulled the door while she pushed, and just managed to pull her out. I must have been given extra strength", she said.

By daybreak, Mrs Pilley's bedroom was completely open to the skies, and by midday the skies themselves had opened, with a long downpour which saturated the exposed furnishings of the 43 evacuated tenants.

Mrs Irene Stevenson, a former mayor of Christchurch, had to move from another Highcliffe block, along with the 72 other residents. She had to leave almost everything behind. But in the morning, just before the rain came down, a friend rescued for her the illuminated scroll which commemorated the day she was given the freedom of the borough, and a photograph of her in her mayoral robes.

Further east, the holiday settlements of Selsey Bill were laid waste in the same way. A few miles inland, the noise of the storm woke Mrs Jacqueline Mitchell-Heggs, all alone in Coates Castle, a piece of Victorian Gothic deep in the woods near Petworth. Afraid the windows would blow in, she got up and closed the shutters.

"Suddenly upstairs I heard first a very loud rending sound, and then a huge thump, and the ceiling came down on top of me. A piece of the chimney, which must have weighed a good ton, had come through the roof and landed on my son's bed in the room above. I'm sure that bed saved my life.

"I fled out into the garden, with the idea of getting into the car and dashing away. But I saw a neighbour had a light on, and I ran to them. There must have been trees crashing down all round me, but I never noticed. What was so very strange was that it was so warm. I just flew out of the house in my pyjamas, and yet I didn't feel a bit cold."

The contrast between the cold air lying over Britain and the warm air pouring up from Biscay was so marked that in places the temperature rose 20 degrees in a matter of minutes, with intense associated up-draughts. Towards dawn, it dropped again almost as sharply, as the spinning depression drew in cold air from the west behind the turbulent mass of warm air. Midnight was easily the warmest time of the whole day.

In Chichester, part of the upper parapet of the cathedral was dislodged and fell through the roof, breaking a stained-glass window. Further east again, Brighton Pavilion was under repairs, wrapped up like a giant Fabergé Christmas present in blue plastic sheeting. As the Pavilion's superb elm trees were thrown down all round it, and the whole town shook as if in the grip of an earthquake, the Pavilion's blue wrappings were torn to shreds. They forced the scaffolding they were attached to out of true. One section moved 18 inches and dislodged the two-ton tip of one of the Pavilion's fanciful minarets, which fell through the painted and gilded dome of the Music Room and half-buried itself in the floor.

The Music Room, once the most beautiful room in the palace, had only recently been fully restored after an arson attack in 1975. The crowning touch in the restoration had been the laying, nine months before, of a copy of the original carpet – a sumptuous piece of Regency Chinoiserie, with a galaxy of stars, mythical birds and dragons on a blue background. The hand-knotted carpet measured 40 feet by 60 feet, and had cost £90,000. The stone knob crashed through its centre, tearing it badly and making a dent like a lunar crater in the floor.

The Isle of Wight suffered early, and suffered hard. By 2.30 am it was already apparent to the miniature county's council officials that a calamity had occurred, and they set about creating an emergency centre to co-ordinate efforts. Two senior highway engineers were put in charge. At least 300 trees had come down across roads alone, and far larger numbers in other places where their carcasses could be left to lie for the time being. Homes, hotels, schools, greenhouses and caravans were plucked and buffeted by gusts which seemed to be reaching insistently for any weak point at which they might be torn apart.

2.30 am was the time when trees beside a caravan site in East Cowes began to keel over one by one, smashing a dozen of the vans; half an hour later the first of a dozen trees fell at another site in Freshwater, destroying ten vans and damaging others.

Coastguards alerted the police in Cowes when they saw that a boat in the marina had gone down. A family with a two-month-old baby and a four-year-old had been living on it, and a hasty search was mounted before police found them sheltering in a public lavatory.

It was also 2.30 am when a family of four fled from their house in Newport, in the centre of the island. One of its gables was beginning to collapse, and dozens of sharp edged slates were cascading into the bedrooms.

"The roof started coming off, slates were falling through it and bricks were flying round like butterflies", Mr Norman Mitchell told a reporter from the *Isle of Wight County Press*. He grabbed his terrified children, six-year-old Laura and ten-year-old Lee, and led them downstairs and out of the building. Then he returned to collect his wife Gillian. He called the fire brigade and three tenders arrived within 45 minutes. The firemen struggled for five hours in the ferocious weather conditions until they were able to pin the roof down again: Mr Mitchell called them " heroes".

In Ventnor, on the south coast of the island, a chimney crashed through two storeys of number 35 Alpine Road. Mr Peter Stephenson, who had been under treatment for a heart condition, was in bed in the first-floor bedroom.

"I suppose I was half asleep", he told the local paper. "I got the rubble off my bed and felt my way along the wall to the door. If I had gone to the centre of the bedroom I would have fallen straight down the hole in the floor. I didn't know it was there."

With an almost personal animus, the gale sought out the Sandown flat of Miss Heather Humby, a South Wight councillor who had just been appointed a member of a special team to handle civic emergencies. Breaking the windows, it made for her files, and siphoned batches of official letters, bills and personal papers out into the darkness, along with her four Siamese cats.

Stories of the same kind could be multiplied from Shanklin, Newport, Ventnor, Seaview and almost every settlement in the island and indeed in towns and villages right along the southern coast. But one of the most astonishing feats of sheer muscle power that the storm accomplished anywhere on its journey was done at Blackgang, near the southernmost tip of the island, where the two-storey White House Hotel had its entire roof lifted away. It was not one of the flat roofs that proved so vulnerable elsewhere, but a substantial twin pair of pitched slate roofs with some lead sheathing – a structure which can scarcely have weighed less than 20 tons.

The owners, Ken and Rita Smith, had spent a frightening night securing doors and windows against the gusts, when suddenly the windows shattered and the whole building started to shake.

"We hurried downstairs for safety as the whole roof took off", said Mr Smith. "It went sailing into a field behind the hotel, 150 feet away."

The couple did not dare to venture outside because slates and slivers of glass were still being blown everywhere. Telephone and power lines were down, so that they had to remain shivering in the wreck of their home – and livelihood – until first light, when Mr Smith made his way to a public telephone and called for help.

With a natural force of this ferocity on the loose in the fields and suburbs of England, it seems almost miraculous that so few people died. Instead of wonderment at how many roofs soared away, and how many chimneys and centuries-old trees were blown down, one is inclined to feel a greater wonderment at the number of roofs, chimneys and trees which survived.

"Trees had come down around us as if a giant had gone walking through the woods", the owner of a damaged hotel in Shanklin declared, feeling for words to express the widespread feeling that some conscious being of superhuman strength and mischievously psychopathic temperament had been out and about on that extraordinary night.

Back in Highcliffe at 3 am, a fire engine was driving along Lymington Road on its way to an emergency call. Its six-man crew had already been out battling with storm damage, and after repairing the damaged roof of a factory at Christchurch, they had been ordered to another factory where the fire alarm had gone off. It proved to be a false alarm – the distinctive wild music of the storm in most urban areas included the shrill note of meaningless fire alarms set off by damage to their circuits. But the crew never got there.

Just as the engine was passing, a twelve-ton tree toppled over and fell directly onto its driving cab. The four firemen in the back were sent flying, and all four had to go to hospital to be treated for minor injuries and shock. But the two men in the cab, Fireman Graham White and Sub Officer David Gregory, were both killed outright. It took their comrades an hour to release their bodies from the wreckage, with the help of a back-up crew sent from Christchurch.

Both the dead men had been volunteer firemen. Mr Gregory, who was 47 and had been with the fire service for 27 years, was a water board employee. He was married, with a 16-year-old son. Mr White was 46, and had 22 years' service with the brigade. He worked as an engineer. He and his wife Susanne had two sons, aged 23 and 12. Mrs White, a nurse, told the press next day that she had begged him to give up his retained job.

"I hadn't been well, and I wanted us to spend more time together", she said. "I don't think there was any way I could have stopped him. He lived for his firefighting. It seemed like we never saw anything of each other.

"The odds must have been a million to one. If it had been a split second different the tree would have fallen in front or behind the cab."

Other motorists died in the same way. Near Salisbury, 18-year-old Anthony Burton was killed when his Volkswagen struck a tree. Near Petersfield, Hampshire, John Barton, a 35-year-old accountant, set out to drive home to Beacon Hill, near Hindhead, at about 2.30 am. The inquest was told that he had been at the stables with a friend who was anxious about a horse of hers, which was suffering from the colic. Five hours later, Mr Barton's car was seen half-buried in the foliage of a fallen tree, with its driver dead inside it. It took a team of electricity workers several hours to cut him free, and it was several more hours before he could be identified.

Even in these western districts where the storm broke first, however, it arrived so late at night that most travellers were already home and tucked up safely – relatively safely – in bed. It is a challenge to the imagination to picture what its impact might have been if it had arrived when the rush hour was under way in the cities, or when school buses were on the move.

In the morning, when people began to try to get a measure of what had come upon them, they could not tell how bad things were. By then, thousands of acres of the South-East were covered in deep thickets of entangled branches and foliage, scorched brown by the salt wind. It was as if a net had been thrown over the territory overnight, trapping everyone underneath it, hampering any kind of movement, and compelling them to cut their way to freedom. Those who gazed out across the tons of debris surrounding them, so dense that in places it was hardly possible to see that such a thing as a road had ever passed that way, must have wondered just how many crushed cars and dead bodies were lying hidden beneath it.

CHAPTER 6

CASTAWAYS

*"I am not fond of expecting catastrophes, but there
are cracks in the universe."*
(Rev. Sydney Smith (1771–1845): *Letter*)

I had it in mind at one stage that it would be good to organize this story on a
systematic basis of chronology, so that incidents which happened simultaneously could be linked, and I could return again and again to individual
stories and take them a stage further each time. The reader could then follow the fortunes of each embattled victim, and get to know them as they
came into view once again.

You can envisage how it might have worked: "At the very moment that
Silas Merryweather saw his prize sow sailing away over the barn, the Dean
of Barchester peered out of the wildly rattling casement of the Deanery
breakfast room, and witnessed . . ." (some diabolical ecclesiastical devastation: to be checked with Dean) ". . .while Miss Heather Humby, whose
four Siamese cats blew out of the window in Chapter Five . . ." etc.

As a virtuoso display of mastery of the course of events, it would have
been stunning. As a readable story I think it would have become incompre-
hensible. There were just too many irons to be kept in the fire , brandished
momentarily, and then thrust back again. And I soon realised that in any
case the materials for a consecutive narrative simply did not exist. Sometime between two and three in the morning, things just began happening
too fast.

It was about 2 am when the trees started to go down in the Isle of Wight,
and about 3 am when the firemen Ernest Gregory and Graham White were
crushed to death in the cab of their fire engine at Highcliffe. It was not later
than 2.30 am when Ronald Davies was killed by a chimney falling through
four floors of a hotel in Hastings, fully 100 miles to the east. By 2.30 am,
too, the London Borough of Camden had already called its tree surgeons
out on the streets, and the high-voltage power lines from Dungeness were
"tripping", as flying debris or the flailing of the cables began to cause short-
circuits, presaging the power cuts which were soon to throw most of the
region into the dark.

By then, the destruction of centuries of parkland husbandry on the old
noble estates of seven counties was well in progress. Thousands of incredu-

lous witnesses were wide awake and pulling on their wellingtons. More stories than any chronicler could begin to assemble, hair-raising, pathetic, grotesque, heroic and tragic, were simultaneously beginning to unfold.

At first, these stories were typically stories of isolation. The stress of the emergency, and very soon the failure of communications, meant that every endangered family, every bewildered group of victims, found themselves faced at first with a crisis in which they were spiritually as close to the predicament of Robinson Crusoe as many of them would ever be: human beings on their own in face of the indifference of nature, and forced to make shift as best they could.

It was as if they were castaways, though scattered throughout an area as amply provided with all the aids and comforts of civilisation as any in the world. In their predicament, the details of events elsewhere were at the time not of much consequence. They were all faced with the same great imperative, to survive and ensure the survival of the people immediately around them, and until they were safe, the significant world was narrowed down to what was relevant to this overriding need. It was nothing to Silas Merryweather what had become of Miss Humby and her cats, nor vice versa, since neither could be of the least help to the other. And even in retrospect, it will never be possible to say whether the sow or the cats blew away first, because in the numbing moment of challenge, most people were far too preoccupied to glance at their watches.

Very soon there was a great change, and the emergency which had separated people brought them together in ways which were for some almost equally memorable and unfamiliar. But at the height of the storm every story was separate, and most stories were oddly similar – the night, the din, the fear, the isolation, the falling timber and masonry, the coming of dawn and a wider appreciation of what had happened.

After that, a great variety of new stories began – the story of the restoration of mainline services, the longer story of linking isolated communities into the network again, the sad story of tidying away the ruin and counting the damage, the acrimonious story of who was to pay for it all, and the slow story of the planting of a new generation of trees. Some of these stories involved complex interactions between the private and public, and indeed international, realms, and some of them are only in their early chapters even now, a year after the catastrophe.

But at 2 am on October 16 everything began happening at once. On the weather map for that moment, it is illuminating to draw a line around the area in which the mean wind speed was more than 40 mph (with gusts of course very much higher). The line encloses an oval shape moving northeast, almost as wide as the Channel, with its 200-mile longer side stretching roughly from Start Point to Dungeness, and on the point of crossing the English coast.

No-one can see the wind, but if one wanted to depict the storm as an entity capable of being visualised, this oval shape, travelling rather less fast than the winds inside it, and very roughly the size of Wales, is possibly the

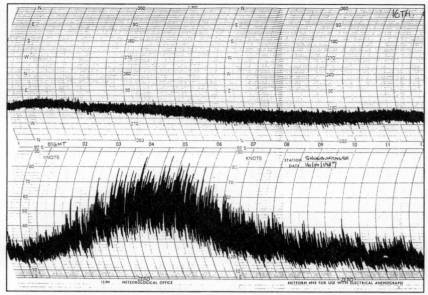

Wind records from Shoeburyness, (Essex). The upper line shows the wind's direction. The lower line shows its strength in knots. For 2½ hours from 0310 GMT the wind scarcely drops below 60 knots (68 mph), "Violent Storm Force 11".

nearest one can get. It crossed that whole length of coast almost at the same moment; Portland and the Isle of Wight must have caught it first, but there can only have been minutes in it.

Three hours later, its leading edge was cascading across London and the Thames Estuary, and spreading as far west as the edge of the Chilterns, like a great torrent or lava-flow across flat terrain containing nothing to resist its advance. The weather station at Shoeburyness, on the opposite side of the Thames Estuary, recorded its first gust of more than 60 mph at just 3 am. By then the outline of the 40 mph wind area had changed shape to a curious constricted, waisted form, like a stream gushing through a narrow gap between rocks, and churning into foam as it does so.

The centre of the low-pressure area had moved on now from the Eddystone to Bristol, and was at about its deepest. It had taken an unexpected turn to the north. Out over the Irish Sea, cold air was hurtling over the Wolf Rock from the north, striving to reach the centre. Warm air drawn by the same impulse hurtled up from the south over Kent and Sussex. Both bodies of air drove insensately on, doomed to by-pass their target to the right, under the influence of the same force which spins water eddies.

If the low point had not strayed further north than expected, the torrent of air from the south would have passed up the Channel on its same blind impetus. But instead it, too, was drawn north – across the centre of southern England. The air there had been exceptionally cool, and so provided no buffer against its flow.

As if squeezed between twin barriers, like invisible cliffs thousands of feet tall above the Dorset and Normandy coasts, the torrent poured through the narrows and out towards East Anglia and the North Sea, where the contours of air pressure allowed it to spread on a wider front as it advanced. As it rode up over the cold air before it, it would gradually began to mingle with it, cool and lose its force.

But at 2 am it was still gathering in pace, turbulence and destructiveness. The land onto which it was moving was unaccustomed to any such visitation. The Weald of Sussex, Kent and Surrey is a tract close to the sea, but not maritime; a tract close to London but even now not altogether suburban. It is sheltered, up to a point, from the perils to north and south by two barriers of chalk, the North and South Downs.

The South Downs make a majestic wall against the sea and its weather, and the North Downs make a barrier of sorts against the commuter – assisted by a combination of Green Belt regulations and excessively tiresome steep little roads designed with a view to exclusion. The Weald's railway towns are commuter towns, but their hinterland can still be uncannily remote. Every dusting of snow cuts the whole territory off from civilization altogether.

The descent from the North Downs is also one of the steepest prosperity gradients anywhere in Britain. Kent and East Sussex, which show so many outward signs of wealth, are among the ten counties with the lowest *per capita* income anywhere in Britain. London, of course, has easily the highest. The statistic is slightly misleading, because it lists workers by their place of work, not by where they live. Commuters working in London raise the actual average considerably. But for non-commuters, this sharp disparity of wealth emphasises the psychological distance between London and the Weald.

In climate, the Weald is a protected haven – sufficiently mild, sufficiently dry, fertile within limits but more remarkable for diversity. The reason for this is geological. The whole almond-shaped valley, 70 miles long and 30 miles wide, is fundamentally the soft underbelly of a great dome of chalk raised millennia ago from the sea under which it was formed, and then eroded away for millennia until it was worn through at the top. The inner domes of softer clays and sandstones beneath it were eroded more easily and exposed in dual cross-section – here on the way up, there on the way down again – while the harder edges of the original chalk dome continued to jut up protectively to north and south.

"Weald" means "forest": it is the same word as German "*Wald*". Of course it is not a forest at all, although it used to be. It is, if you like, the ghost of a forest, covered by the ghost of a chalk dome. At least, I am inclined to envisage Lamberhurst and Goudhurst, Hassocks and Sissinghurst and Burwash, all such pleasant and immaculate and cherished places, as spread out in perpetual sunshine under the shelter of a huge, airy, invisible snow-white dome – like one of those Victorian arrangements of choice varieties of birds or small animals displayed in natural attitudes under a dome of blown glass in the parlour.

If so, the Weald lost its roof on October 16, as did many of the lesser hot-houses and enviable dwellings that it embraces.

Land of any kind is a protection against storms. As long as a storm is over the sea, it siphons up water whose cooling supplies it with the heat to keep its engine running. Simple friction between the wind and the rough surfaces it rubs over on land tends to sap the strength of the lower levels of moving air. High ground, against which the same lower levels can exhaust much of their momentum is an even better protection.

In a prevailing airstream where the gales come most often overland from the west, or south-west obliquely across the coast, this geography has served to foster in Sussex and Kent the development of a splendid and distinctive natural scene. The social history of the area ensured that men would bend their best efforts over many generations to exploiting these natural advantages, in accordance with their changing conceptions of productiveness, convenience and splendour.

There are historical as well as climatic reasons why the concentration of charming towns and magnificent houses in this area is so exceptionally high. Very probably it already had this character in Roman times, when it was densely settled and prosperous. In one sense, it has been commuter-belt country for many centuries: it was a natural place for feudal magnates to put down roots if they wanted easy access to the capital – even when the time-scale was a day or two, rather than an hour or two. Any king would be concerned that an area which would be the most direct route of assault for an invading enemy from the Continent should be well defended, and under the control of men he could trust.

In early periods, when the forest was still extensive enough to harbour outlaws, and any row between in-laws could lead on to armed skirmishes, the great houses of the Weald retained much of the character of fortresses. Penshurst and Ightham Mote are examples. Knole, too, is a transitional case – to my mind, the richest and most evocative of them all. In later, quieter times, when comfort and display took precedence, the greatest builders often preferred to look for larger elbow-room further away from London, but Petworth, and Uppark on the downs at the Weald's western extremity, are as fine as any examples of these later houses.

Apart from the mild climate, the Weald possessed those two essentials of early industry – iron and timber. The iron was mined from the sandstone strata exposed by the erosion of the chalk dome, and the timber provided charcoal for smelting it. Eventually, tree-felling for iron furnaces made such inroads on the forest that it was seen to be necessary, in the days of Charles II and John Evelyn, to resort to policies of conscious conservation.

It became part of the role of an enlightened landowner to develop and remould the remains of the old hunting-forests, for profit and the adornment of the estate.

The finest parks and gardens of the Weald were the product of two centuries or more of careful and far-sighted management. The standard tended to falter in the late nineteenth century, and recovered somewhat after the Second World War. The outcome was a heritage of mature woodland, planted as much with an aesthetic as a business eye , perhaps the richest concentration anywhere of examples of that art of landscaping which has been claimed as England's only distinctive contribution to the list of fundamental genres in art.

In the last resort, it should perhaps be considered as an extreme case of the art of flower arrangement. At least the weather was about to give a brusque reminder that its essential materials, being alive, were inherently ephemeral.

North of the North Downs lies that great bowl of mud on which London is built, with all its spires, pinnacles and skyscrapers, and its great dome (unfinished when the 1703 hurricane passed by, so perhaps never exposed before to a comparable blast), its radio masts, gangling builders' cranes and armies of plane trees.

Epping and Hatfield forests on London's opposite fringe are the remnants of ancient woodland, with old hornbeams, once pollarded but left for a century to grow into strange half-crippled shapes. Beyond them lies the Breckland, with miles of undulating sandy heath, once forested but cleared of trees by neolithic colonists working with fire and stone axes from the great flint factories at Grimes Graves nearby. Once cleared, it was too dry, cool and acid of soil either to make good farmland or to be recolonised by trees, and it lay almost disregarded until it was planted with conifers in this century.

Beyond the Breckland stretch the once-placid but much-changed river valleys where John Constable learned his art, and the dark fenlands of Norfolk and Suffolk, merging away imperceptibly into the North Sea – an artificial landscape created by centuries of drainage and intensive, highly profitable agriculture. All this human effort paradoxically produced a landscape especially rich in distinctive wildlife.

East Anglia's population fell sharply in the eighteenth century, in the time of the enclosures, and it became a dank mysterious backwater until only a few years ago, when people and businesses began to flood in to take advantage of its space and closeness to London. This variation on the theme of nature's abhorrence of a vacuum has made it the fastest-growing region in Britain.

This territory north-east of London is more remarkable for fine towns and churches than for rich men's mansions, though it includes Hatfield House, which possesses the wreck, still just alive until about 20 years ago, of the oak under which Mary Tudor's sister was said to have been sitting in 1558 when she was told that her sister was dead and that she was Queen of England. The eccentric Hervey mansion of Ickworth, a Greek Revival gasometer, attended by noble cypresses until October 16, is a few miles further north. In the far distances of Norfolk stand Blickling Hall, one of the most attractive of all the Elizabethan great houses, admirably adorned by its woodlands – and the majestic if intimidating later masterpiece of Holkham Hall.

The great storm took the garden of England unawares. It came with a more southerly slant than gales usually do, and struck inland directly from the sea. It came saturated with moisture and brine swept up from the wave-crests in the Channel, and it came at a moment when the landscape happened to be already in an especially vulnerable condition.

The year had already been a fierce one. In January, southern England had one of the worst winters in memory. London had its coldest day since 1940: it was so cold that the bell of Big Ben froze and refused to sound. As for the Weald, there is something about its convoluted geography which makes it seize up at the least trace of snow. Now, with really heavy snow-falls, it became Britain's Pole of Inaccessibility. For two days even the substantial town of Sevenoaks was cut off by road. Trains and buses were cancelled, and temperatures dropped to 27° Fahrenheit. Some of the smaller settlements in the area, on the outer foothills of the North Downs, were cut off for a week or more, and had to be rescued with snowploughs.

Then in March, a gale blew over southern England. There were floods and landslides, trees uprooted and power lines severed across much of the country. Thousands of homes were blacked out, and churches and schools were damaged. Gusts of more than 100 mph were recorded off Lands End, and the Severn Bridge was closed for only the second time in its history. Large headlines recounted the damage, which was at its worst in Cornwall, Devon and Wales, but also caused deaths as far east as London and Norfolk. Three men were killed when a van hit a fallen tree in Banstead, in Surrey.

Twelve fatal casualties were listed in one night – a smaller number than the 19 recorded for the single night of the October storm, but one of the same order. The March gale struck in the morning, when people were out and about, and children on their way to school.

In the autumn came rain. The rivers of the Weald were on the point of overflowing. In Kent, the rainfall for October had broken previous records even before the storm arrived. Police and council workers that night were already keeping an anxious lookout for signs of flooding. The soil had soaked up as much moisture as it could contain. As a result, it provided a less firm base than usual for the roots of the trees growing in it.

In addition, the trees still had their leaves. Like a ship still carrying full sail, a deciduous tree in full leaf is far more at risk of being capsized by a sudden squall than it is when it has reefed down for the winter. Its surface area exposed to the pressure of wind is several times as great as that of a leafless tree.

It was the chance combination of these three factors – the saturated soil, the leaves and the direction of the wind – that made woodlands which had stood for hundreds of years so very much more vulnerable on October 15 than they had been in the many gales that they had ridden out in their time.

It was not even as if their leaves were beginning to turn gold. When a leaf's supply of sap has been shut off by the scar-tissue which grows across the vein in its stalk at the due point in the year, it is half ready to let go its grip on the branch as soon as a strong wind blows. But that day the trees were still green, with only a few minor boughs just beginning to show the sere and yellow leaf. Autumn had not yet begun for them. But there was not to be an autumn in the Weald that year.

CHAPTER 7

"THE TEMPEST"

"The principal task of civilisation, its actual raison d'être, *is to defend us against nature."*
(Sigmund Freud: *The Future of an Illusion,* 1927)

Peacehaven is one of the strangest places in England. It is anything but a haven in the literal, maritime sense, and on the night of October 15/16 it was anything but peaceful. It is spread out at an altitude well advanced towards the stratosphere, on top of a wall of cliffs cross-sectioned through the South Downs – a frontage without one scrap of comfort for any vessel which might attempt to seek refuge there.

Peacehaven does not feel like a town, for it lacks a town's central nexus of mingling activity; nor does it feel like a suburb, because Newhaven is out of contact behind the hill. With its grid of streets going nowhere, it has the air of something imposed, a cantonment in alien territory (it used to be known as Anzac-on-Sea). Where the houses run out, the streets simply fade away in rutted tracks and wire fences.

It is Valhalla with net curtains, a settlement created by soldiers returning from the 1914–18 war, understandably a little surprised to find themselves still alive, and eager to try the novel experience of a bit of peace. They staked their small gratuities on a stretch of downland, and covered it with innumerable bungalows far away above the strife and troubles of the world.

Back in a land fit for heroes to live in, they passed the quiet hours embellishing their new homes. Seventy years of do-it-yourself have left it with the highest incidence in Western Europe of fretted eaves, pergolas, whitewashed birdbaths, and gnomes drawn up in platoons. It is easy to scoff, but the place is only a democratic expression of the same impulse to adorn the ancestral demesne which grander families lavished to the gratitude of us all on Petworth, Knole and Leeds Castle.

The south country is not just a sweep of stately homes, half-timbered villages and hop fields: it is also a great concentration of get-away-from-it-all-architecture. People will pay anything for a flimsy flat with a suggestion of a view of the sea, or a caravan which has been a stranger to the open road all its life – though very apt to take to the skies in a stiff breeze.

The whole coastline from Selsey to Beachy Head is not far from being one linear conurbation of sea views, alternately posh and plebean, with just enough downland left between them to walk the dog on. Like that smaller ribbon development between Bournemouth and Highcliffe, where many of the events of Chapter Six took place, it has a high ratio of retired people among its inhabitants. This side of Kent and Sussex life suffered as severely in its way as the historic countryside, and perhaps at as great an aggregate cost in grief.

Peacehaven took as bad a knock as anywhere; worse than anywhere else I saw. All along that cliff frontage, so naively trusting of the goodwill of nature, there was hardly a home left undamaged, soon after the storm. Tiles had been rasped away from the ridge and corners of almost every roof, as if someone had scratched them off, digging his fingernails in under their edges. Sounds of drills and hammers were everywhere as workmen hurried to get the damaged houses weatherproof again.

Almost every house had a window boarded up or a wall shattered, with sagging tarpaulins stretched over the hole to keep the rain out. Sometimes a whole row of big windows built to face out over the wide spectacle of the sea had been smashed. Lightly-built glazed sun lounges had collapsed in splinters. Big patches of stucco had been sucked away from cream-washed walls in ugly blotches.

Sometimes a gable end had been torn down, leaving the ridge of the roof sagging down onto the tops of the walls. The vanished gable might be on the seaward side or on the opposite side, away from the blast. Whole roofs had lifted off or fallen apart. In one or two houses the whole upper storey had virtually been sliced off: the houses on either side would quite possibly be almost unscathed.

One house had had its garage demolished and two picture windows upstairs smashed. One of them was double glazed – a system which, as the television advertisements show us, is so resistant that you can batter it with a chair without cracking it. Through the empty eye-socket of the window, one could see the bedroom inside, and a picture on the wall of HMS *Victory* under full sail on a sunny sea.

It is no mystery why Peacehaven suffered so much. Everyone with a sea view on that coast paid dearly for it that night. But Peacehaven, perched up above the world like another Shangri-La, was in an airstream of its own.

Wind blows harder above ground level. Close to the ground, it is slowed by friction, but at higher levels it can run freely. If a wind gauge set at the Met Office's regulation height of ten metres records a mean wind speed of 60 mph – which would put it officially into the category of a "Storm Force 10" – a man standing on the ground, two metres tall, would have his hair ruffled by a wind of only 40 mph, a lightish gale. The strength of that same wind about 60 feet above the ground would be 65 mph, or Force 11.

Peacehaven stands on cliffs about 100 feet above sea level. At an elevation of 100 feet, the normal speed of the wind is 25 per cent greater than the speed at regulation height for a wind gauge. If a gauge records 60 mph, that means that the wind must be blowing at 75 mph at an elevation of 100 feet. That is the equivalent of "Hurricane Force 12".

It is debateable whether one should think of "ground level" in the Peacehaven situation as the level of the beach or of the cliff-top. The sea exercises relatively little friction on the passing air – only as much as serves to lick the waves into shape. What is certain is that masses of air in violent motion must have rushed across the sea and come full tilt up against the flat wall of cliffs. They had nowhere to go but upwards. Thrusting up, breaking apart, causing back-eddies to pour into the pockets of low pressure they left behind, they created a vicious turbulence which pounded and plucked mercilessly at the homes on the cliff-edge.

Even at sea level, the wind had the force to do an effective demolition job. Five miles east of Peacehaven stands Seaford, on land where a marsh once lay behind a shingle bank heaped up by the tides. The chalk begins to rise again in a gentle slope towards Beachy Head, six miles away. Sea-view construction has reached out to the foot of the downs, where several rows of modern houses stand virtually on the beach.

Even Seaford is commuter land, because it has a station – a draughty enough platform at the best of times. After the storm, this platform exhibited one of the more eloquent witnesses to the character of the force which had passed through.

It is lit by a row of fifteen or twenty double strip lamps, raised on steel poles of the usual pattern. Modern street lamps, pylons and the like stood up rather well to the storm on the whole. They are simple resilient structures with which nothing much can go wrong, and their design is carefully tested to stand up to all foreseeable stresses. Most of the poles on Seaford station had borne the blast unscathed, but six had been permanently bent by it.

Next to a pole which had not bent were two which had been left just slightly out of true. Next to them was one which had tilted rather further. After that came a pole which had been bent a full twenty degrees, and must have been not far from collapse. After that, a pole similar to the third damaged one. After that, a pole similar to the first and second.

Here was the visible profile of one of those arbitrary gusts mentioned by so many observers. Its message was as unmistakeable as the bellying out of a wind-filled sail. There appeared to be no structure nearby which could have caused any particular turbulence: the poles marked with graduated precision the passage of a gratuitous jet of air 80 or 100 feet wide and exerting forces beyond the tolerance of modern engineering design.

The houses under the eastern cliff were examples of modern engineering design, too. Terry Buckley is one of Seaford's commuters: he teaches ancient history in a north London school. He lives close to the site of a burial-ground used by the Romans for 200 years, but closer still to the sea.

Cliff Close is a short cul-de-sac lined with flat-roofed terrace houses, built in the late seventies. Mr Buckley's house backs onto the sea, 30 yards from the beach, and has three storeys.

"I was sleeping quite heavily until about 2.30 am, when the phone woke me up", he says. "It was my next-door neighbour. 'Can you hear that banging?', he said. I was aware a very strong storm was blowing, and I could hear a tapping, but I didn't really take in the importance of it, and I soon went to sleep again.

"When I woke up again, the whole house was shaking. We sleep on the top floor, next to the study, which looks out over the sea. I went into the study and saw that the ceiling had sagged down, so that it covered half the window."

He went back and woke his wife, Sue. "She was in a catatonic trance, she couldn't move at first. Then she went towards the study, and I said: 'Don't go in there', because we had just had it redecorated, and it would have been a shock. I got her gently to the stairs and down to the ground floor."

Their children, seven-year-old Sean and five-year-old Erica, were already on the ground floor, in a room opening onto a lowered patio which offered some shelter on the seaward side. "They had been a bit disturbed, but they weren't really awake – a bit muzzy. I gently got them out of the room and along to the hall, which seemed the safest part of the house. As the storm got more intense, we got under the stairs.

"The children weren't especially frightened. Sean just kept talking all the time – mostly about football. I think he had the feeling: 'I've got Dad's attention here, let's make the most of it.' In the end I had to say for the sake of my nerves: 'Just keep quiet a bit, things are rather difficult at the moment.'

"Children are phenomenal – either they're all over the place or they're totally impervious to what's going on. I was putting on a very *sang froid* air, I suppose. Inside, I was churning up like mad – 'What am I going to do to save my family?' The most they did was to say quietly: 'This is awful, Daddy.'

"At 4.30 the power went off. It was the peak of the storm. I was afraid then the house would come down. I went back to the first floor, which is an open-plan living area with a glass sliding door looking out on the sea. It was double-glazed, but you could see the glass slightly bowing inwards. I thought: 'If that goes, it'll rip you to shreds' – and we didn't go back in that room again.

"When I saw the sea, the waves were coming in so hard I could hardly believe it. It was quite dark by then, but you could see it clearly, because the white surf itself was so bright.

"Then there was an incredible crash. Our next-door neighbour's roof came off as a unit and took with it half the top floor. Their windows came out and crashed onto the concrete. It was the end house – the neighbour who had phoned me earlier. I didn't see where the roof went – it went 30 yards down the road, and knocked a caravan over – and two cars were a write-off.

"We simply did nothing. I didn't know what to do. I didn't dare go out, and the walls were shaking like an earthquake. And there were the panels flying about."

The panels were a feature of the design of Cliff Close, and of many other homes built in recent years. From a distance they look like wooden weatherboarding, but they are plastic, which does not rot and does not need to be painted. They are tough, about a quarter of an inch thick, and ribbed – for strength, and in tribute to the memory of overlapping timber planking. They are particularly favoured near the sea, where they protect the bricks from the salt.

The gale had enormous fun with such panelling, all along the coast. It tore it up like paper and carried long coiling sheets of it through the air – much further than it could have carried fragments of glass from broken windows, which could scarcely have been any more dangerous.

"The stuff was ripped off and flying down the road. It would have cut you in half if you had tried to go out", says Mr Buckley.

The disappearance of most of his neighbour's top floor meant that the partition wall between their two houses became in effect the end wall of the block, exposed to all the violence of the weather. Hidden by fitted cupboards in the study, a half-inch gap developed between this partition wall and the wall facing the sea, leaving the house apparently intact but actually wide open to rain and subject to further collapse.

The noise all this time was so numbing that the family were quite unaware until morning of another roof which had taken to the air in the night, only a few yards away. At the other end of Cliff Close, on the same, seaward, side as Mr Buckley's house, stood a row of four garages, with brick walls and a flat timber roof. Opposite them, on the landward side, was the home of Bruce Arthy, a pensioner living alone.

"The first warning I had that anything special was happening was when shingle started pinging against my bedroom window. I sleep upstairs. We face straight down the Channel, nothing in front of us till you get to the West Indies. One gets used to storms over the years – I've been here 16 years – but I'd never known that to happen before."

The shingle must have flown at least 100 yards, because Mr Arthy's house is further from the beach than the Buckleys'. "I got up and dressed, and came downstairs. I sat here on the sofa facing the window, waiting for the windows to blow in. The lights were going on and off, but I had an emergency lamp beside me.

A slight man in a cardigan, he sat for two hours on his grey plastic sofa, surrounded by breakable mementos, facing towards the invisible threat. Just behind him was the kitchen, which is turned the other way; he cannot say why he did not go and sit in there.

"Then at about 5 am there was an awful crash and all the internal doors in the house burst open – just from the force of the wind right through the house. Then there was the thumping of blocks falling down.

"I stayed where I was until it started getting light. The wind was still very strong. I looked out – and I couldn't see anything !"

The roof of the garages opposite had flown clean across the street, doing half a loop-the-loop on its way, but leaving no mark on the ground. It had struck Mr Arthy's house at first floor level, bursting his bedroom window and wrecking the room (if he had stayed in bed he would probably have been killed). It came to rest leaning on the house, bottom uppermost, cutting off the daylight from the downstairs lounge. It rested partly on the glass front porch, which was almost unscathed, with a pot of geraniums still blossoming inside it.

"This window wasn't damaged at all – and my car in the garages wasn't even scratched – a pity: it could have done with a write-off! Some of my neighbours further down the road were even worse hit. I'm 69 years old – but I think that night put five years on me!"

Just up the hill from Cliff Close is Cliff Road, a similar street lined with counterparts of its houses in the style of about 20 years earlier. They were damaged almost as badly. One house, with a picture window boarded up, a glass-sided balcony battered as if with a hammer, and a garage visibly tottering, had on its gate the name "The Tempest".

This was too good to resist. "A south-west blow on ye And blister ye all o'er", Caliban hissed in Shakespeare, as if summoning up this very salt-blast to scald the people of Sussex.

Mrs Chris Stanley appeared at my knock, brushing aside gaudy draperies hung all around the stairwell. "Costumes", she explained. "Finishing them off. Come through to the sitting room".

The sitting room was decked with costumes as well, and hand-drawn posters announcing : "Seafield Youth Drama Group".

"The hurricane had a touch of humour, you see", said Mrs Stanley. "We were going to do 'Shelter for the Homeless' in the street next day, for One World Week, but the costumes blew out of the house when the window went, and we had to give it up."

Several ducks were calmly sifting the mud in the back garden, beside the stricken garage.

"All our house was in bits, and I was expecting to find the ducks blown away in the morning . . . the roof of their shed had gone. There are six ducks, and two nanny goats . . . I milk them . . . I used to make cheese, but it has to hang in a muslin bag in the kitchen for ages, and people kept knocking their heads on it.

"I'm psychic, or so I'm told. I was aware beforehand that something was going to happen. It was like an eerie foreboding calm. My youngest son felt the same way . . . he was in the other front room. I said before I went to bed that I didn't like it that there were no curtains in my bedroom.

"In the night I heard a whizzing and humming and saw things flying past the window, and the electricity was going on and off, so I hid under the bedclothes. Really gigantic pieces of things were just being lifted up in the air – tiles – things that looked really solid.

"Then my son came in and said 'Mum, I feel really frightened with all the glass in my room.'

"I said 'We'd better get your father downstairs, then.' Jack is six foot four and weighs about 20 stone, and he was pretty deeply asleep, because he'd come in late from a party – so that was a job.

"As we were doing that, there was an enormous crash. All the tiles at the front blew off, and the attic door and window blew out, as well as the bedroom door on the first floor. Now the wind had got inside the house, the window on the stairs began to go – we could feel it pulling. We tried to tie it by the handle to the banisters, but it was no good.

"There were four of us trying to hold onto it, but it went all the same. And all our costumes stored in the attic began whisking out through the hole. All these green sleeves flying past us in the dark – it was like having a poltergeist in the house.

"We were worried about the ducks, so Jack tried to go out and see. But there was so much pressure on the door that it took three of us to open it – and when he was out there, he could hardly move. No sign of Prospero and the other ducks – we didn't know what had happened to them until the morning after.

"We all just crouched in the back sitting room after that, listening to things go. It was fantastic – never ever have I come across a storm like that."

As I left, Mrs Stanley warned me not to visit a badly damaged house further up the hill. An old lady lived there alone, and was still too distressed to talk about the experience. At the last moment, I remembered to ask her about the name of the house: why "The Tempest"?

"Oh, because of its situation, and because I've been an actress, and because we've got a drake called Prospero . . . I don't know."

The stories of the Buckleys, the Stanleys and Mr Arthy are just three from an area about a hundred yards across. Until the wind dropped, each household was virtually isolated in its confrontation with the storm, even though in ordinary conditions their homes were no more than a few moments' walk apart.

Their stories could be duplicated in thousands all along the coast. In Bexhill a block of flats called The Marlowes was unroofed, and more than 40 residents had to be evacuated. Cyril John, who is disabled, was dragged by his wife from his top-floor bedroom only a few seconds before the ceiling whisked away. At another block, St Thomas in West Parade, Captain Mark Smith reluctantly yielded to a neighbour's pleas and left his penthouse flat, 20 seconds before the penthouse was tossed into the street six floors below.

Thirteen-year-old Angela McEwen, of Linden Road, Bexhill, woke to find two tons of rubble on the landing outside her bedroom door. Nine-year-old Anthony Bryant of Burgess Hill, near Brighton, had an even narrower escape when a falling chimney sent rubble tumbling right into his room. His home was in a pub called "The Cricketers": another pub of the same name was damaged in the same way in Hastings.

The spire of St Luke's United Reform Church in St Leonards was lifted from its place and lowered intact, almost tenderly, into a side aisle of the church, like a giant ice cream cornet. A section of roof had opened up like the lid of a box to receive it. The walls of the aisle were badly damaged, and a triple-arched gothic window below was all but destroyed. But the cross on the top of the spire was not even bent by its giddy descent.

At Saltdean, Brighton, residents of the Taynham House flats fled for fear that their homes would collapse. A block of flats under construction at Rustington, in Littlehampton, was reported to have collapsed "like a house of cards". The large flat roof of the William Parker School, St Leonards, had its upper layers torn away. Two surgical wards of Bexhill Hospital had to be evacuated because cracks appeared in their walls, less than 24 hours after the local health authority had reprieved them from closure.

A chimney stack was brought down in Cooden Drive, Bexhill; a tree fell across a roof in Dunclutha Drive, Hastings; and houses had their gable ends neatly taken out in Wrestwood Road and Ninfield Road, Bexhill.

It would be easy to fill the rest of the book with addresses in this way, without moving more than a mile or two from the coast. Everywhere there was shock, bewilderment and terror, with damage to private and public buildings, crushing of cars, tearing down of hoardings and signs, blocking of road and rail, bursting of shop-windows and ravaging of woodlands.

For two hours the wind blew with rising force and increasingly wild transitions between gusts and lulls; then it blew for two hours at its utmost extreme of force and variability; then, after about 6 am, it began to diminish in strength at about the same rate as it had risen . On the wind meters it traced out a rising and falling curve, gracefully symmetrical over the hours but insanely jagged from minute to minute. At the observation station at Shoeburyness, there was a period of three hours in which its velocity never fell below 55 mph.

Marjorie Doddington had been up late getting ready for her daughter Marion's wedding reception, scheduled for the day after next. The freezer of her house at South Cliff, Bexhill, was as full of food as it could be. The house was flat-roofed,and dated from the mid-1920s. Marjorie and her husband Bernard had cleared two big rooms downstairs and laid out one trestle table. More tables and chairs for the sixty guests were on order for the next morning. She had put off starting to lay out the tablecloths and glassware until the other tables arrived. The bride would be coming from Dorking, the bridesmaids from Northampton.

"I was woken by the noise and got up, but after an hour I thought I might as well go to bed and stick it out. Then there was a tremendous bang on the roof. I put my head under the pillow. Then the ceiling fell all over the bed.

"All I could think of was the Tebbits – you know, after the Brighton bombing – those television pictures of them getting him out – and her injuries. I thought I'd better get somewhere safe. Bernard was already up and on the staircase. We went down and stood in a sort of passageway in the hall. We felt a bit safer. Then there was another bang, and the whole roof was sucked away. It went right over the rest of the house, over a hedge which must be 20 feet from the house, and landed in the street.

Then the rain began to come down, soaking everything. I said to Bernard: 'Go and get the keys of the car from the bedroom drawer – we can sit inside it." He went and tried the door, but it was jammed. So we just settled down in the driest spot we could find."

They had no way of telling how widely the effects of the storm had spread. For all they knew, Marion in Dorking would still be making preparations in the happy expectation that everything would be ready for the great day in Bexhill. In fact, Dorking had suffered badly, too, and by daylight it was obvious there that the trip across the Weald was as out of the question as it would have been to take a wedding party across the Upper Amazon basin. But the telephone lines were down, so parents and daughter were unable to get into contact.

It was slightly later, at about 4 am, that a tree on The Ridge, Hastings, gave up its battle with the wind and leaned on the side of the Robert de Mortain public house, a white-walled, high-gabled pub built very solidly in about 1860. Steve Thomas and his wife Heather had taken it over the previous June: it was their first business. They were woken up by the jolt the tree sent through the building, and came downstairs from the top floor to make a cup of coffee.

"It was lucky it was coffee. If we'd been drinkers, we'd have been over the other side of the room, at the bar, and – and then we wouldn't be here now !", says Mr Thomas.

"Our two-year-old son Andrew was still asleep upstairs. We wondered if Heather's Dad was awake and I went to see. He was, and he came to join us. Ten minutes later there was an almighty crash and the place filled up in a split second with dust – you couldn't see a foot in front of your face.

"Heather screamed and I ran upstairs. I got to the top of the stairs more by feel than sight. Andrew was standing there at the top, and I just pressed his head to my chest and ran."

What had happened was that a chimney stack had fallen through the roof, through the family's lounge and kitchen and the function room where Mrs Thomas's father had been sleeping, through the bar and down into the basement, destroying everything on its way. Rubble fell onto a bed in Andrew's room next to the one he was sleeping in, but he was untouched.

"Heather's father and myself struggled together to get the front door open, but the wind held it shut. When we got outside, we went to the car – which was rocking around on its springs in the wind – and drove to where a member of our staff lives. We spent the rest of the night there."

It had been the narrowest of narrow escapes. If their movements had differed by only a few paces, or if the trajectory of the chimney had been different by just a few feet, all four of them might have been killed. When one considers how many people were sleeping under vulnerable roofs, gable ends and chimney stacks (chimney stacks above all), and how many such features were damaged by the storm, the number of more or less narrow escapes must appear astonishing.

These are the stories which can make one feel at times that the storm was a great blustering tease, which played brutal practical jokes on some of our cherished treasures, and delighted in inflicting terror on the human midgets in its power, before capriciously letting them off. But of the thousands briefly swallowed up by the storm and trapped in its circumscribed world of tumult and danger, there were a few for whom that experience was followed by no escape.

Down the hill from the Robert de Mortain, Hastings itself was getting a bad battering. The trees in Alexandra Park were buckling like straws. On the seafront, where a rather forbidding cliff of shoulder-to-shoulder hotels beetle like tenements over the shingly promenade, rows of beach huts were being comprehensively mangled into firewood. The fishermen who still go out with nets in open boats from Hastings beach were struggling to haul the boats up the shingle and further from the waves.

The Queen's Hotel, Hastings, still has more of an air than most of its fellows. It dates from the first half of the last century, when it was the undisputed premier hotel of the town. Most of the chess grandmasters of this century have made their way to it at one time or another to compete in the Hastings Chess Championship, still one of the major events in the game's calendar, in spite of the bleakness of the resort in the off-season and the increasing dowdiness of the hotel's reception rooms.

There were only 65 guests in the four storey hotel on the night of October 15/16. As it happened, all three rooms at one rear corner of the hotel were occupied. In Room 430 on the top floor slept Ronald and Gladys Davies, an elderly couple from Warwickshire, visiting the seaside for an autumn break.

"We are used to gales along the seafront, and at first I thought this was just another one", says Berthold Berger, manager of the hotel. "I was asleep in my flat, which overlooks the sea. The first thing I was aware of was when my window went. The whole thing crashed in – there was glass all over the room. That was about 2.30. Then I thought I'd better go down to see if everything was all right.

"I found that the glass roof of a lift shaft had fallen into the foyer. I went towards the back of the hotel, and I heard shouting. Someone was calling from up above. I found that a chimney stack had fallen through all four floors".

The four-ton stack had carried away the floors of rooms 230, 330 and 430. Broken water-pipes snaked out into the void at each level and sent thin cascades of water down onto a a pile of debris below.

"One gentleman was clinging on between the second and third floors and shouting. We climbed up and were able to rescue him. He was in a state of shock, and he was taken to hospital, though they were able to discharge him later. But we saw that there was a lady in the mass of stuff at the bottom. She was caught between two mattresses, and they had protected her. She had fallen from the third floor and ended up between the first floor and second floor. We couldn't release her ourselves. The fire brigade came, and it took them three hours to get her out – ten hours before they had finished working there."

The lady between the mattresses was Mrs Davies. Her husband had shared her fall, but he had not been so lucky. She survived, but when the mess was cleared, he was found dead underneath it.

CHAPTER 8

A STORM IN A TEACUP

"Naturae enim non imperatur, nisi parendo."
("To control nature, you must obey it.")
(Francis Bacon: *Novum Organum*)

Those blotches where stucco was torn from the walls at Peacehaven looked as if they had been sucked off: and so they had. Pull, not push, is the most effective tool the wind has in breaking up buildings. It has a repertoire of special effects which produce a wide variety of different kinds of havoc, but the basic processes at its disposal are only two: push, and pull – which is the other side of the same coin.

Push is perfectly easy to envisage. Along comes the wind like a double-decker bus run amok – for a storm weighs more in total than fleets of buses, and can apply an overall pressure equivalent to the weight of several buses to the side of a single large building. It careers full tilt into whatever stands in its way, and if it is a tree, say, or a hoarding, it may knock it down flat.

Swift, dynamic and simple: the irresistible force meets the immovable object, and the object proves not so immovable after all. But if push is all there was to it, all the tumult of the air on October 15/16 would have done very little damage, and scarcely any to buildings. If that was all there was to it, aeroplanes would not be able to fly either, but luckily they do.

The wind is not really very like a double-decker bus, of course, because it does not arrive like a bus does, all in one lump. Even as the maximum gust comes screaming in upon a house, the air is all round the house, and inside it, too. The air is really more like a river. It flows past the any obstruction, which stands like a rock in mid-stream. It parts on either side and meets again behind. The house is wrapped up in air, almost cocooned by it.

The impetus of the total mass of moving air may be prodigious, but the amount of force it can bring to bear on any one point is small, because each point it presses against is more or less bolstered up by the air behind it, and because air is really so very tenuous.

Push without pull would not have much effect, but push and pull, or pull and push, can be lethal in a diversity of combinations. As it flows round a structure, the wind can suck away stucco, tiles, gable ends and the outer skin of cavity walls by a subtle application of force more effective than any crude shove.

Although it is not difficult to see that air flowing turbulently round a structure must exercise forces of suction in places, the exact processes involved are puzzling. This is one of the reasons why the damage a storm leaves behind can seem so paradoxical, so malicious – as if it had had some cruel joke in mind in selecting things to smash or to spare.

There was the roof of All Saints' Church, Hawkhurst, Sussex, for instance. It came through the night without serious damage, except at one point – the very spot that one might have thought safest, because it was sheltered by the tower. In fact, it was the very suction set up by the air flowing round the tower that enabled the wind to drag the tiles up there and toss them away.

The sharp eye of Defoe noticed similar things in 1703: "However it was, it appear'd in some Places, the Windward side of the Roof would be whole, and the Leeward side, or the Side from the wind, would be untiled."

Or an even more striking example. An aerial photograph showed a double avenue of trees on a farm near Sevenoaks. The wind came at it from the side, and all eleven of the trees along one side of the avenue were thrown down. The trees on the other side had their smaller branches shredded, but all survived (illustration, page 115).

But it was not the trees on the windward side which failed, although it might appear that they would be bound to bear the brunt of the onslaught. It was the ones on the other side – the very ones one might have thought would be protected by their partners.

It would be necessary to inspect the avenue closely on the ground to be sure what had happened. It is possible that there was some difference in the firmness of the soil on the opposite sides of the track. But other cases bear out the probability that the trees on the leeward side were literally sucked down, while their opposite numbers just survived.

When a single tree goes down, it is impossible to say whether it was pushed or pulled down – the symptoms are the same. But when the leeward tree of a pair is the one to fall, and the same happens in a whole series of cases, that is evidence that pull did the job. If the wind had been a little stronger, of course, then the windward trees would have gone too, as happened in many other instances. Then people would have said in the morning: "See how they fell on the others and brought them down as well."

These suction effects, and the way they take their hold on buildings, have necessarily been a matter of close study to architects and structural engineers.

"Around a tall building, the speed of the wind on the leeward side can be three times what it is on the windward side", says Dougal Gonsal, chief engineer of the London Borough of Camden. "Wind tends to accelerate towards the edges of surfaces. The greater the velocity, the lower the pressure. This is what gives rise to the suction forces which do the damage."

The fact that pressure is lower where the current runs faster may seem puzzling. If a house stands in the full current of the gale, like a rock in a stream, then the air has to travel further in flowing around it than air which is cruising past uninterrupted. It has to increase its speed, or there would be a drop in air pressure at the back of the house. Since nature abhors a vacuum, it will be drawn onwards all the more urgently to fill up that zone of low pressure. The whole cause of there being a storm at all is exactly this imperative desire that impels air to rush in towards areas where pressure is lowered.

So far so good. But common sense seems to dictate that if there is a stream of air, and an object in mid-current diverts some of it to left and right, the pressure where it is diverted should rise. In effect, one would expect the air to be squeezed at the edges of the side facing the wind, and the edges of the roof. Instead of congestion, there is a thinning-out: the pressure there is less. Anyone looking at the damage done by the storm could see that it had been less, but might be at a loss to see why.

Daniel Bernoulli explained how it must be so. He came from a large and quarrelsome Swiss family of mechanical *savants* in the 18th century, and his father, Johann, was so inveterately jealous of his own son that he threw him out of the house when the Paris Academy awarded them its gold medal jointly. He considered that the honour should have been all his own. If his son's theory had been imperfect, Johann would certainly have disproved it out of spite.

Fundamentally, Bernoulli's principle is an application of Newton's second law of motion, the one that says that a golf ball goes a long way when a golfer hits it, while a boulder would go less far. Energy is converted into different forms in different situations. Where a fluid is drawn more swiftly through a narrowed space, some of its pressure energy is converted into kinetic energy (energy of movement) and so its pressure drops. The upper side of an aeroplane wing is more curved than the under side, so that the air flowing across it has further to go. It flows faster, and therefore has a lower pressure. It is the lower pressure above the wing which sucks the plane upwards.

There are various ingenious classroom experiments to demonstrate the Bernoulli effect. One of the less messy is a gravity-defying display recommended by Mr Gonsal. Take an old-fashioned wooden cotton reel, with a hole drilled through its axis in the usual way. Cut a piece of card to a disc the size of the flat end of the reel. Stick a pin through the card and rest the card on the reel, with the pin hanging loosely down the hole. The purpose of the pin is simply to stop the card slithering off the reel sideways.

Hold the reel above your head and blow steadily through the other end of the hole. The air will rush along it, and one would expect it to blow the card off the other end. If you blow carefully, it will not: on the contrary, you can lower your head as you blow until the disc is pointing at the floor, and it will remain glued to the reel until you run out of breath.

The force that holds it there is the suction created as your breath streams through the narrow space between the card and the reel. The faster the current flows, the lower its pressure, and the stronger the suction holding the card in place. The same force, produced by similar circumstances, is the one which tore off the stucco as the wind gushed between the bungalows in Peacehaven.

The ingenuity of the wind in applying this principle to create different effects was inexhaustible. It was able to demolish gables, whose tips are at the vulnerable edge of the wall surface, by drawing them outward until the brickwork was curved so far that it had to shatter. In some lightly constructed buildings, the bonding between gable tip and roof structure is not strong, so that there is little to prevent the brickwork from being pulled away.

Once a gable had gone, the wind could rush inside the roof space. Pressure inside would rise, adding its push to the pull of the suction constantly in play over wide areas of the outside of the roof. If the fastenings were not strong, the whole roof could be lifted bodily away.

Something slightly different must have happened in the remarkable case of the White Hotel on the Isle of Wight, mentioned in Chapter Five. There were no flimsy brick gable ends to carry away there, and the roof was a massive construction firmly bonded to the rafters, though possibly not to the walls. Its total weight cannot have been less than 20 tons. The owners described how the windows shattered and the house began to shake. Then the entire structure of twin pitched roofs and ceilings rose up as one unit and was carried 150 feet into the field behind the hotel.

The air pressure inside the hotel would have been lower than outside in the middle of the side which faced towards the wind. That must have been where the windows burst. Air would then have gushed in, raising the internal pressure. In combination with the suctions already operating outside the roof, this must have produced a lifting force capable of raising the front edge of the roof a little.

As soon as the roof lifted, the wind was able to thrust in under it, and make it soar upwards like an aeroplane wing. Prodigious forces were required to lift such a heavy roof, but it was only because push and pull were deployed in exactly the right way that they could achieve what they did.

The experience of the Stanley family in Seaford (chapter seven) shows how human muscle power can be overwhelmed by these suction forces. When the internal pressure in the house was higher than the outside pressure at the back , all their efforts could not stop the staircase window from bursting outwards. Even after the window had gone, it took the efforts of three of them to get the front door open against the internal pressure holding it shut.

Imbalances of pressure between inside and outside can work either way. In 1986 the Building Research Establishment published a study of storm damage which showed two photographs side by side. One was of an unfinished warehouse where the wind had flowed in through the unglazed window openings. It had blown out the rear wall, weakened by suction forces behind. The other picture was of a similar building where a door near the edge of a wall, in a suction area, had been blown outwards. The drop in internal pressure was so sudden that the windward gable of the building collapsed inwards.

Flat roofs, which tend to develop suction forces all over their upper surface, are particularly apt to turn themselves into aeroplane wings. A great many collapsed, in France and the Channel Islands as well as in England. Mr and Mrs Doddington in Bexhill lost the flat roof of their 50-year-old house while the other houses around it, with pitched roofs, lost only tiles.

The effects of pressure were reinforced by the relentless shaking the wind gave to buildings for hour after hour, trying push and pull alternately as its eddies came and went – testing the structure incessantly to see if some small weakness could be worked on and turned into a major one. Several chimneys gave up the battle when the storm was already moderating, and they must have ridden out many gusts stronger than the one that finally defeated them. For instance, Beryl Agha and Patricia Bellwood were both to die only an hour before sunrise.

The strangest thing of all, perhaps, is that the forces that caused so much destruction were in some respects remarkably slight. The difference in atmospheric pressure between the deepest depression and the sunniest high-pressure zone is small in comparison with the change in pressure one experiences in walking to the top of even an English mountain. Of course, the alternations were very sudden, and their effect was multiplied by the huge volumes of air involved.

But the violent changes in pressure that provoked such terrifying gusts seem to have been almost imperceptible to the human senses (though they may have contributed subliminally to people's sense of shock). Barry Keenan, a worker in a fish and chip shop in Brighton, was one of the few who even mentioned this factor in describing the events of the night: "The walls of this building were moving as if they were being punched by big fists", he said. "Nothing could have lived outside. Inside, the air was moving so badly through displacement that your eardrums were being hurt."

As far as structures are concerned, architects have been intensely aware of the problem of pressure on buildings since the Ronan Point disaster of 1968, in which five people died when the entire corner of an East End tower block collapsed after a small gas explosion. Pressure from an internal explosion is theoretically the same thing as suction from outside of the kind induced by the wind: it is the other side of the same coin. But though similar in kind, it is very different in degree.

A household gas explosion can create a momentary pressure of up to 12 pounds per square inch. A cubic foot of water, for comparison, bears down on the base it is standing on with a pressure of half a pound per square inch. A load-bearing panel in a tower block therefore needs to be able to withstand an outward pressure equivalent to a column of water 24 feet deep. That means that the panel should be able to bear the same pressure it would meet if it were the floor of a water tank 24 feet deep. Of course, roof spaces, windows, chimney stacks and the like are not designed to bear the force of a gas explosion, nor could they be.

The force that wind can exert is slight by comparison with gas. "We don't bother about wind forces if we've allowed adequately for gas", says Mr Gonsal. "One usually designs for wind forces of only 10–15 pounds, not per square inch but per square *foot*. That is the equivalent of a column of water only four inches deep".

A column of water four inches deep may sound ridiculous. In practice, it is more formidable than it sounds. The weight of four inches of water adds up considerably over a large area. When the Stanleys of Seaford were trying to open their front door, it was as if they were trying to lift it upwards while it was lying under a sheet of water roughly four inches deep. The overall weight of water, about 35 pounds, is enough to make the task quite a bit harder.

But it is an odd thought that all that shattered timber and masonry, all that damage to houses, trees, communications – and disruption to the very framework of society – was caused by a force which at no single point exceeded the force exerted by a cupful of tea on the bottom of a teacup.

CHAPTER 9

THE SEVEN OAKS

"I have seen Tempests, when the scolding winds
Have riv'd the knotty oaks . . .
Against the Capitoll I met a Lyon,
Who glaz'd upon me, and went surly by . . ."
(Shakespeare: *Julius Caesar*)

The seven oaks of Sevenoaks came in the days after the storm to stand as a kind of epitome in the public mind of all the losses that it inflicted. There had in fact been two sets of seven oaks planted in the town in an emblematic spirit. Seven Turkey oaks, now in their prime, had been planted along the edge of the Vine cricket ground in 1902, to mark the coronation of Edward VII. Seven more were growing up as a reserve team just across the road, planted after the war as a gift from Canadian airmen stationed nearby – mere forty-year-old striplings. Six of the seven full grown trees came down on October 16, and three of the younger ones. Out of a double holding, the town was left without so much as a quorum.

Pictures of the felled row of great oaks went round the world. Keith Spencer-Allen lives in the downstairs flat in one of the Victorian houses overlooking the cricket ground. He was in New York on business at the time. When he opened a copy of *The Independent*, he was agitated to see spread across seven columns of the front page a photograph of the six great trees churning their branches in their death agony, with the home where he had left his wife and baby apparently in the midst of them. He was at the telephone in no time.

But the gale had treated the habitations of men tenderly. The foliage literally brushed the fronts of the houses, but they were unscathed. Mrs Penny Spencer-Allen had a friend in to stay while her husband was away: "Neither of us slept. The sound was like trains roaring past – and there was all this crashing, smashing noise going on all the time. The lights went off at 3 or 3.30. At about 4 I said 'I can't stand this any longer', and I got up. I looked out of the sitting room window. It was pitch black everywhere, and I became aware that a tree had come down. I didn't believe it – I thought it must be just a branch."

On the third floor, Mrs Sandie Wade was in bed about 50 feet from the tree's upper branches. "The noise of the wind was horrendous. The three children slept right through it, and I just put my head under the pillow and hoped it would go away. My bed was moving – trembling. It started about one o'clock. In the end I got up. The power was off, so I lit a candle and made myself a cup of tea. It was about twenty to five by then."

The deep booming of the wind was incessant, intimidating and exhausting. A constant unidentifiable rattling from all directions kept the nerves on edge, as one waited for something that mattered to work loose.

The Wade children slept later than usual in the morning. In the end twelve-year-old Christopher called out: "I've been awake for ages, but its so dark, I haven't got up."

"Then I looked out of the window", says Mrs Wade, "– and it was full of tree !"

"We all started jumping around – the two younger children were clinging onto me with fright. The girls and I just stood weeping with shock and sadness – we couldn't believe it had happened.

"The tree had come down a little sideways, on a different line from the others. The wind must have been . . . swirling. If the tree had come down straight it would have come through the front of the house.

"But the extraordinary thing was that the noise was so deafening that neither I nor any of us heard that tree come down !"

It came so close that its branches smashed a Victorian lamp which stood at the front door. Neither the Wades not Mrs Spencer-Allen had heard a sound above the general din.

Trees were falling unnoticed on both sides of the house. In the garden behind, a large pine selected a narrow passage between the Baptist Church and the Church Hall, and subsided into it, heaving its roots upwards through the floor of Mrs Wade's garage – one of the few buildings to have been demolished by a falling tree from underneath, as the loss assessor observed when he called.

In all this, the gale was true to type. For all its frenzy, something seemed again and again to inhibit it from doing all the damage that it might have done. For all the lost roofs and trees left sprawling across battered gables, it is remarkable how little harm the trees did, considering the quantities of timber thumping down across seven counties.

Between Weald Road and Brattle Wood, Sevenoaks, a stretch of wooded common lay between two rows of houses which backed onto it, a hundred yards apart. Down this alleyway between homes, one of the gale's characteristic squalls or williwaws had gone rampaging, leaving several hundred trees scattered like chaff. It was awe-inspiring to reflect on the damage it would have done to the houses and the trees close to them if it had passed a few yards to left or right.

Trees fell all along the road north out of Brighton, but they lay obediently along the verges, clear of the houses bordering the road. It was natural here that the south wind should throw them northwards, along the line of the road. Yet on the road from Brighton to Hove, which runs not north but west, the casualties seemed again to pick out resting places where there was no house to land on, as if they could see where to fall.

Observers disinclined to put all this down to Providence wondered whether some effect of dynamic airflow might have steered falling trees away from buildings, Bernoulli notwithstanding.

The noble parade of elms past the Brighton Pavilion and along the Old Steine was a particularly hard loss. East Sussex had succeeded in saving many of its elms at the time of Dutch elm disease in the 1970s by bringing to bear all possible means of protection, from spraying and injecting to instant removal of affected branches. Scores of survivors had been kept alive into an age when a grove of elm trees had become a rarity, only to be trampled down now by the storm as it burst in off the sea.

The damage to urban trees was often as great as that in the countryside, and perhaps a greater source of grief in the days that followed. Alexandra Park in Hastings was left almost unrecognisable. Handsome trees which had adorned the Pantiles in Tunbridge Wells keeled over, their roots erupting up through the paving stones. Trees have been planted more enthusiastically in many towns in recent years than in the country. But the storm found out their weaknesses mercilessly.

Planting needs skill, patience and advance preparation. On many new housing estates, their bareness hastily mitigated by the application of gangling nursery trees, these conditions were absent. The roots of nursery-grown trees are apt to develop as a sort of ingrowing clump, timidly remaining within the imaginary confines of the plastic bag they first unfold in. Unless they are teased out into bolder configurations, the tree can grow quite large without any proper extension of roots, and a brisk wind can throw it down with ease. Pouncing round the edges of tall buildings which channelled and concentrated its force, the gale contemptuously tossed aside these flimsy gestures in propitiation of disregarded nature.

The havoc to garden fences, sheds, greenhouses and in particular to cars and garages in towns and villages was immense. But the most significant impact that the unseen multitudes of falling trees had was on communications, as cables were borne down and roads and railway lines blocked by ranks of heavy trunks, sometimes as many as ten in a mile, creating not so much barricades as extended carpets of densely enmeshed branches.

Some families were unlucky in the lottery of falling boughs, however. Trevor Bardell, who had been so impressed earlier in the evening with the unnatural warmth of the night, lived outside Wrotham, Kent, in the house that he and his wife, Wendy, had had built two and a half years earlier.

"I run my own advertising agency from an office in the garden, and when the wind got up, I was afraid a tree might come down on that. The noise of the wind was horrendous, but what woke us up was the flashing from overhead power lines which had broken and were lashing around. I spent most of the night roaming round the garden with a torch, watching the trees.

"My office was scarcely touched, in fact. In the end we were so tired that we went to bed. Wendy decided not to take our six-year-old daughter Clowey to school, and was dozing beside me. The wind was still roaring away. It was about 6.15 am.

"Then there was this noise. I was asleep, but I heard it in my sleep – I remember it so well! It was like when you're on a building site, and you hear a tipper lorry drop a great heap of rubble – a sound you feel as much as hear.

"Wendy saw daylight through the roof for a moment, and then it went dark again. The ceiling came down – a big bit of plasterboard came down on me first of all, and that protected me as tiles and bricks came showering down on Wendy. She was cut round the head quite badly – superficial cuts, but lots of blood. She was on her feet in a shot in a sort of reflex. We were rushing round bumping into each other in a complete flummox.

"Clowey came rushing out of her room crying. It was split from top to bottom, though nothing came through. We had a cousin staying with us, and she picked Clowey up. I was just rushing around with nothing on – you can't get your priorities right – do I get dressed, or help my wife, or go to my daughter?

"A beech tree overhanging the house had come down right in the middle of it. We had it measured afterwards – it was 125 feet tall, and when the crane finally lifted the trunk off, after the branches had been cut off it, it still weighed 10½ tons. A branch like a spur had come through our bedroom ceiling and almost touched the floor – if the bed had been under it, we'd have been killed. The whole top storey of the house had been pushed two or three feet backwards. On the outside walls, you could see that the bricks had been forced into a curve.

"We had no power and no telephone. I have a car-phone, so I ran to the car, which was badly damaged, but still usable, and I rang 999. The police said: 'Even if you're reporting a murder, there's absolutely nothing we can do'.

"Our neighbours were wonderful. They were banging on the door within 1½ minutes, and we stayed with them for four days till we could find somewhere to go.

"One strange thing. There were lots of glass lamps in our room, so the floor was covered with broken glass. When we went up there later in boots, you couldn't take a step without hearing it crunch underfoot. But we had been running all over the room in our bare feet, and neither of us had a scratch on our feet."

The detail of bare feet on glass can be counted as another of the special oddities of the storm. Charles Winder, a bank manager living a few miles to the south, at Little Mill, near Tonbridge, recalls the same thing: "We jumped out of bed in such a panic that we never noticed the floor was covered in broken glass. We only realised afterwards – but our feet weren't even scratched."

His 300-year-old converted farmhouse stands on rising ground about 100 yards behind a line of large pine trees. The noise of the storm woke them soon after midnight, but it seemed to reach its maximum intensity at about 4 am.

"We were just thinking of evacuating the front of the house when we were hit. We could see the branches of the pine trees bending in the wind, and as they snapped they were being carried all the way back to the house – massive great boughs which took a crane to remove. They weighed up to half a ton.

"Our eldest daughter Harriet, who is four and a half, came into our room because she was frightened, and five or ten minutes later a branch came through into her room and smashed her bed to smithereens. Our room was damaged too, but luckily it is a long room, and our bed was right at the back of it. Our other daughter, Lucy, who is two and a half, sleeps at the other side of the house.

"The house was shaking, and if it hadn't been a timber-framed building I think it would have been demolished. The brickwork was damaged, and there was about an eighth of an inch of dust all over the house next morning. But the timbers absorbed the shock. Every window at the front was broken."

The family took refuge in the kitchen at the back of the house, a room with massive roof beams which Mr Winder thought offered the best protection. They sat and listened while the wind rampaged through the house, pulling pictures and plates off the walls. A rumble from the library told them that its high brick chimney had collapsed.

"The noise – I can't describe it. One just hasn't experienced anything one can compare it with.

"We just sat it out. We had a bottle of wine in the fridge and some milk for the children. They were in a panic – really, so frightened that they wouldn't let me or my wife Christina get up even to go and see what was happening in the next room. We sang songs they had learned at nursery – 'The Wheels on the Bus' was a good one, because you can keep improvising new verses.

"Even with daylight we still couldn't venture outside at first. The radio had gone, so as far as we could tell it was just us who had been hit. There was a pattern like a sort of funnel across the grass, as if a whirlwind had gone over it. And everything had gone black – all the leaves."

Such accounts give some impression of the tumult of the night. Many victims had no means of guessing whether they were the unique victims of a freak whirlwind, or whether the whole of southern England was in the process of being blown into the North Sea.

Trees were being mown down in the dark like regiments of infantry exposed to withering machine-gun fire in no-man's land. Sometimes they yielded one after another, weakened by one gust and demolished by the next, sometimes they fell in ranks to some gust of pre-eminent intensity. The tree that fell on the Bardells' house had stood its ground through the worst of the wind, and fell at last to one of its final peaks of effort. At Chilham Castle, near Canterbury, a 300-yard double avenue of 150-year-old limes were seen to fall within three minutes of one another, without a single survivor remaining.

Chilham Park also contained what was said to be the oldest recorded heronry in Britain. "It is about 860 years old and is recorded in the Domesday Book", Lord Masserene and Ferrard told the House of Lords during a debate on the storm. "Some of the herons return on St Valentine's Day, and I am worried that if they do not return then some terrible fate will befall me. I do not know what to do, because every tree has gone. Beech trees of a great height have all come down. I shall try to erect artificial nesting sites, but I do not know if the herons will use them."

Eddie Hare, who runs an aviary and hospital for birds of prey at Chilham, spent the night watching helplessly as the wind shook and and tugged at his cages. His house was damaged by a falling tree and lost a chimney stack as well. The aviary contained about 50 hawks, falcons, eagles and owls , some of them injured birds he was nursing back to health or using for breeding. Others were trained fliers which he used for outdoor demonstrations and lectures in schools.

"I couldn't get near them – everything had to wait until morning. I lost twelve birds, as well as nine aviaries and all my weatherings, which will cost about £2,000 to repair. Some of the birds were permanently injured ones missing a limb or an eye. Some literally walked away into the bushes. I got one of them back nearly two weeks later – a female kestrel with a damaged eye. She had managed to scrape by, but she was on her last legs. From the mud on her beak, I think she must have been living on earthworms.

"Others were carried away on the wind. There were a pair of goshawks which were extremely valuable, worth £2,500 as a pair. They will probably survive – find a niche in the country somewhere. Possibly they may still come back. They're identified – not long ago I was able to hand a goshawk back to its owner after it had been lost for more than two years."

As for wild animals and birds, it is a matter for mere speculation how they may have fared as the gale passed over. Many areas of woodland were inaccessible for so long afterwards that nothing could be done to survey them for casualties. Even burrowing animals must have been in danger as the root-plates of toppling trees churned up the soil.

Birds panicking in the darkness must sometimes have broken their necks as they flew full tilt into unseen boughs. Instinct may have taught them to lie low, but then too they would have been in danger of being crushed under foliage matted and compacted by tons of wood pressing down on it. It was reported that some starlings were found dead still clinging to their perches, though it is not clear how they died. Some bird-watchers assert that the height at which flocking starlings follow their stereotyped routes is related to atmospheric pressure, as if they have the sensory equipment, which we lack, to detect absolute levels of pressure. If so, then they might have been forewarned of the coming storm.

Many birds were picked up in the wind and carried far from their native feeding grounds. But overall, the casualties of the night among wild species were almost certainly negligible, in relation to the wastage imposed on all animals in the wild in the struggle for existence.

A horse was reported to have been killed at Shoreham when a falling tree broke its neck. But it appears that many farm animals sensed instinctively that they should keep away from large trees, and took refuge in the lighter coppiced woods. It was impossible for instinct to have had similar warnings programmed into it about the danger of electrocution, and near Guildford 13 cows were struck dead in a single field, when a power line came down. The knacker who had the task of taking the bodies away noticed that some of them were not touching the wire at all, and seemed to have been killed by current running through the moist air or the ground.

At Handcross, near Haywards Heath, a brood mare at the Impney Stud was reported to have been so terrified by the noise (which resembled "the roar of jet planes hurtling up the valley") that she had a heart attack and fell down dead.

John Walmsley, a vet at Liphook in that odd area on the border between Hampshire and Sussex where all the place names seem to be curt and harsh (Rake, Steep, Liss, Iping, Stonor, Butser, for instance – Liphook itself evidently being named in commemoration of some very unpleasant fishing mishap long ago) was in the middle of an emergency operation on a horse when the lights in the operating theatre went out.

"It was an abdominal crisis – it might have been an appendix, and we had to open the abdomen, an operation called a laparotomy. The horse had been brought in from West Wittering at about 10 pm, and we decided at about midnight that we would have to operate.

"The protocol for an operation on a horse is more or less the same as it is for human surgery, except that you have a padded cell to anaesthetise them in, and a winch to lift them onto the operating table once they're asleep. You need at least five people to do a laparotomy – two surgeons, an anaesthetist and two nurses.

"It took us three-quarters of an hour to get it to the operating table. We opened the abdomen and found that what was wrong was a torsion of the bowels – an obstruction, a twist – something which can be fatal quite quickly if it isn't corrected. The obstructed part of the bowel had got terribly full, and we were just draining it when the lights went out. Until then we had only been vaguely aware of the wind.

"We had an emergency generator, but it was a mobile one which takes some time to connect up, so we had to finish the operation by the light of torches. We stitched it up and put it on a drip. It was about 4 am, by then.

"We still didn't realise quite what had been going on outside: we set off for home and got as far as the gate. There was a tree across the drive. So we got some handsaws and spent three-quarters of an hour cutting our way through. When we drove our cars through, of course we found there was a mile of fallen trees between us and the road. One came down on my car. So we went back – it was 4 the next afternoon before we could get out.

"The next few days were desperately busy – not because there was such a huge number of casualties, but because it was so damned difficult to get around. Horses seemed to have been quite clever at not getting injured, even when their stables were collapsing around them. We had one fractured femur, which we screwed up – an interesting case. But it was surprising: we've had more trouble after thunderstorms than we did that night.

"No, the horses didn't seem particularly agitated either before or after the storm, though I do believe animals are much more sensitive to changes in atmospheric pressure than we are – when the glass falls, you can count on getting these colic cases in.

"The horse with the laparotomy – that was fine. I rang the owner to tell her about it next day and she said: "That's all right; but I've lost my roof!" The horse was called Amber, but they've christened it Hurricane now".

The keepers at John Aspinall's two zoos in Kent had a busy night. At Port Lympne, near Dungeness, keepers battled their way in along blocked roads to help move animals under cover, with trees crashing down all round. "The animals were very spooked by it all – and they remained spooked for days afterwards", says Robert Boutwood, manager of the zoos.

As the men struggled to secure the agitated animals, the scene was weirdly iluminated by blue flashes from the high-voltage pylon lines linking the Dungeness power stations with the National Grid. One keeper was on his way to check the zoo's rare herd of Przewalski's horses when he became aware of a whistling noise in the air. At first he could see nothing in the darkness. "Then he realised it was corrugated iron peeling off the roof of the horses' shed and flying past over his head – one sheet could have decapitated him."

At Howletts Zoo, keeper Nick Marx was woken by hammering on his door, just outside the zoo, at about 3.30 am. The four or five staff available began checking cages in case falling trees – the zoo lost 200 that night – had broken any of them. Among the animals at the zoo are some which are both valuable and dangerous, like Barbary lions, tigers, and snow leopards.

They found that four Capuchin monkeys were missing, which was worrying because they do not fare well in cold weather. Two clouded leopards had also gone. They were well able to stand the weather, because their native territory in south-east Asia can be quite cold.

A leopard on the loose looks bad in the headlines, even though the clouded leopard is a less alarming creature than its name suggests. It is about one-third of the size of an African leopard, and weighs about 30 pounds. The colouring of the escaped animals is precisely adapted to help them sink into a background of foliage: in the chaos of broken branches it was a hopeless task to look for them before daylight.

"I went on to check the enclosure of our pair of tigers, Khan and Zabel", says Nick Marx. "I saw that a tree had come down on the edge of the enclosure. It had huge branches, there was stuff everywhere. It had crushed the fence and lay like a bridge across the moat.

"Khan was nosing round the branches as I got there. Obviously the quickest way in was to jump on a branch and go over the moat. I grabbed a length of wood and went over with the chainsaw, and began cutting away the branches he might use to get out.

"He was pretty interested in all this and kept coming up close, so I had to watch my back. There was nowhere I could shut him up. I knew I could handle whatever he could come up with. He's a big chap, but I'm on good terms with my animals, and I know him better than anyone else has ever known him.

"There was no time for gentleness and friendship – if he came near I just shouted at him to piss off. I secured the fence as well as I could to keep him in until the welders could do a proper job. I suppose it's more spectacular with tigers, because they're dangerous, but really everybody did a great job that night – it was turmoil, just turmoil."

Khan is a fully-grown male about ten years old, weighing between 400 and 450 pounds. Nick Marx knew him when he was young. And is he a tiger of mild and equable temperament, as tigers go ?

"I've been told to say yes."

CHAPTER 10

PRETTY AS A PICTURE

"The voice of the Lord breaketh the cedar trees:
yea, the Lord breaketh the cedars of Libanus.
He maketh them also to skip like a calf:
Libanus also, and Sirion, like a young unicorn."
(Psalm 29, verses 5 and 6)

The Pleasure Ground at Petworth took 400 years to make, and four hours to destroy. "Destroy" is hardly too strong a word, although many of the trees and shrubs collected there survive, and the determination of the Petworth gardeners will ensure that there are still many beauties there for future visitors to enjoy. In time, it will undoubtedly be possible to reproduce what has been destroyed, for detailed records of the planting in the park go back for more than 200 years.

But the identity of a wood is bound up in a certain changing continuity, and the blow suffered by the Pleasure Ground on October 16 was so comprehensive that it is no exaggeration to say that the entity brought into being by Capability Brown in the 1750s ceased to exist that night, as the wind off the sea fell on its trees while they were still in full leaf.

It tore some of them up bodily, indecently exposing that octopus-star of curling roots which the turf normally covers. It split others along half the length of their trunks, uncovering wood as white and smooth as if it had been freshly planed – or tipped them askew against their neighbours, with the arteries of their roots irretrievably severed. The most eloquent witness to the sheer brute force of the blast was borne by some especially firm-rooted specimens which had been snapped off a few feet above the ground, in a mass of splinters which reminded many observers of bomb damage.

As time passes, the personality of a wood can and must accommodate to the disappearance one by one of even the most salient of its trees; but it is another matter if too many are thrown down at once. A kind of apostolic succession of harmonious renewal is broken. More than that, the disappearance of the major sheltering individuals can alter the micro-climate of the spot so that smaller species are unable to thrive as they did. For a wood is a society in which the presence or absence of each member subtly affects the others.

In the Pleasure Ground it was not only a matter of breaking a succession: many of its sweet chestnuts, limes and planes were the very ones planted by Brown, often grown to an enormous size. They included the largest sweet chestnut ever recorded in Great Britain, and a cedar of Lebanon of almost unrivalled splendour.

The basic character of the garden remained as it had been set by Brown. It was enriched at the turn of the century (a low point for tree planting in Britain) by two successive Lady Leconfields, who planted exotic species like the tulip tree, weeping holly, cornel and the broad-leaved beech, as well as a diversity of old and rare Himalayan species of rhododendron, now transplanted in effect to a new and harsher climate overnight.

Although he laid a masterful hand on the rest of the park, Lancelot Brown did not conjure up the Pleasure Ground from nothing. The Petworth records show that in 1575 there was only a park "thynle sett with oaks and some Beches (and) 72 deare". But by 1610 there was an elaborate garden in the formal Elizabethan style near the house, and a rectangular plantation to the north, divided up by open spaces and labelled on the map: "Birchen Walks", "Sycamore trees" and "Nursery". It survived little changed when the gardens were remodelled in baroque style a century later.

In the five years during which Brown was employed by Lord Egremont as a sort of visiting consultant at Petworth, he worked this plantation up into something very different. He replaced the straight rides with winding gravel paths, built a couple of classical temples and introduced a wealth of the new species which the great explorers of the age were bringing back from far corners of the earth. The garden grows on a patch of sandstone soil in the midst of chalk downland, so it was able to nourish plants sharply distinct from everything round it, and to nurse them to unusual size.

This concentration of natural artifice was so distinctive that a visitor from America in 1811 declared that it was more like a "heavily-timbered American forest" than anything else he had seen in England. "All these trees seem to accommodate themselves extremely well to the climate of England, and not to feel, while growing within the inclosed grounds of a peer of the monarchy, the loss of American liberty."

Many of them were still hale old retainers, now in the service of the National Trust, on the night when the American climate reached out along the jetstream across the Atlantic and put an end to them.

The Pleasure Ground was a special loss because it was very obviously a work of art, elaborated with exceptional care and imagination. The great park around it might more easily be mistaken for a work of nature. If one calls an image of the "English natural landscape" to the mind's eye, one is as likely as not to summon up a scene like the park at Petworth before the storm. The noble groups of mature oaks, chestnuts, beeches and pines gave variety to the rise and fall of the chalk grassland, and made frames to the sinuous lake, in what appeared to be the happiest combination of fortuitous harmony.

Not a bit of it. The park was every bit as conscious a piece of stage management as the Pleasure Ground. The disruption of Brown's carefully calculated dispositions of cover and space extending across a canvas of 700 acres is arguably a greater loss than the damage to the more obviously artificial garden. Petworth park is (or was till October 16) perhaps the most remarkable intact example of the only genre of art which – it can plausibly be claimed – was conceived and brought to perfection by the English.

Landscape is the art which attempts to reconcile the ideal and the actual on the most ambitious scale. There are no more intriguing documents of the interplay between aesthetic and social values than the sumptuous handbooks published by Brown's articulate successor, Humphry Repton: all fitted up with overlapping pages so that the reader could instantly lift a flap to transform a drawing of a sordid horizontal utilitarian scene into a gracious prospect, in which cultivation and culture could be seen to join hands. They indoctrinated a whole generation of landowners in the sleights of hand necessary to reproduce a visible Eden on earth, while expressing the virtues of a hierarchical social order and fostering the latest advances in agriculture.

It was all artifice: the happy variation of large clumps and small; the subtle emphasis on the drama of a hill by a line of woods along the top; the framing, concealment and surprising uncovering of natural features by means of the trees – even the sinuosities of the lake, which had to be manufactured by damming a marshy stream.

The historical context of these particular stands of wide-skirted trees was particularly rich, not only because Brown's own plans are so unusually well-documented but also because the painter Turner drew from them some of his most elegiac landscapes (he was a friend of the third Lord Egremont, and his visits to the house over many years were very fruitful). The massing of the trees themselves, as seen from the front of the house, is said to be an intentional echo of the balances of Claude Lorrain's painting, *Joseph and Laban*, in the Petworth collection.

Thus it was possible to see together at Petworth nature which had imitated art, the art which it had imitated, and a new growth of art which in turn had imitated that imitation. The conjunction will never be quite so sharp in future: live trees have proved, as they usually must, more ephemeral than dead paintings.

The society which created great landscapes like Petworth died long before its trees did. The meaning that the surviving parks have for society today is very different from the meaning they had for their creators. They still represent a kind of Eden, but a fragile and threatened one. In a stretch of country which is among the most densely crowded in the world, the idea of a surrogate Eden takes on more the character of a surrogate wilderness – and wilderness everywhere is under threat.

Petworth itself was under grave threat for years in the 1970s, while a bitter, socially-charged, debate was fought over whether a by-pass should be cut through the acres where Brown had so ingeniously conjured up an illusion of limitless space, to relieve the undeniable traffic congestion in the village uncomfortably squeezed up against a corner of the park's haughty perimeter wall.

Some of its counterparts , like Saltram near Plymouth and Osterley on the edge of London, were spoiled in this way in the post-war decades, when such things seemed to be slipping to the margin of society's concern. Only in the last 20 years has the tide seemed to turn in the opposite direction.

For the people who had devoted themselves to tending and defending the rich concentration of great parks and gardens in the south-east, the gale came with a numbing and bewildering force, the force almost of a betrayal. It seemed a denial of the very idea of harmony between man and nature that the parks appeared to symbolise. It was a blow below the belt – not from the motorways and pollutions of the crowded modern world, but from nature itself.

The impulse to preserve, rather than husband, these revered landscapes – as if they really were paintings subject to conservation – has not always served them well. Over a long period about a century ago, low timber values and the obsolescence of oak as a patriotic investment in the raw material for wooden battleships meant that landowners took little trouble to renew their woodlands. The original trees had leisure to grow ever more majestic, untroubled by the forester's axe, but also unaccompanied by younger trees destined to become their heirs.

After two world wars gave reminders of the advantages of self-sufficiency in timber, there was a hasty revival of forestry, encouraged with fiscal inducements. But it concentrated on quick results, with monotonous plantings of rapidly growing conifers, highly vulnerable to wind damage in their immaturity, with no stronger individuals among them to give protection. It is only quite recently, on the time scale of tree lifetimes, that worthwhile inducements have also been offered for the planting of slow-growing, slow-earning, hardwood species.

In fact, the intensity of the 1987 blast was so devastating that even where there had been active planting, young mature broad-leaved trees were massacred as indiscriminately as their venerable elders and the spindly plantations of living pit-props. But the pattern of history meant that many of the parks and woodlands which were most precious to the public were older than they should have been. They were ripe for catastrophe.

The owner of one of many damaged parks, Lord Montagu of Beaulieu, expressed the idea of a failure in long-term housekeeping when he said afterwards in a House of Lords debate : "Historic gardens and parks, like historic buildings, have always depended for their upkeep on a number of traditional superimposeed cycles of maintenance, from the very regular cutting of grass to the very infrequent replacement of mature trees. The great storm and extensive subsequent survey work by English Heritage have shown that in many well known gardens major cycles of maintenance and replanting have been neglected over a long period."

If a riotous overflow of blind energy like the storm can be said to have something as decorous as a moral, no doubt this was it. It enforced a sharp, and one hopes lasting, change in our perception of the fact that trees in the landscape do not just happen to be there. They need planning, encouragement, investment, and understanding of the different histories of different kinds of wood.

But the reaction to the devastation could be no simple resolve to put everything back the way it had been. Where avenues had been damaged, for instance, there was no straightforward way to restore the symmetrical pattern which had been disrupted. Attitudes, tastes and priorities change.

One example is the famous grove of beeches and pines on the high point of Chanctonbury Ring, on the downs behind Worthing – visible for 38 miles, it is said. The remains of a Romano-Celtic temple lie there, in the midst of a prehistoric earthwork. The trees were planted by Charles Goring of Wiston House (pronounced "Wisson") in 1760, when he was a boy. Every day in dry weather he would carry bottles of water up to the prehistoric earthwork, and water his seedlings. He was not one of those who plant trees only for the benefit of posterity, for he lived to be 90 years old and keenly enjoyed in its maturity the landmark he had created. In the 1830s, at the age of 85, he wrote:

> *"How oft around thy Ring, sweet Hill,*
> *A Boy, I used to play,*
> *And form my plans to plant thy top*
> *On some auspicious day."*

His beeches suffered greatly in 1987, with losses of about 75 per cent. Today, however, planting trees where their roots disturb a prehistoric site is frowned on. No decision would ever have been made to clear the site, but now that chance has partly cleared it, it is likely that it will not be replanted, and that Goring's monument will become a monument to the unknown people who dug the ring.

At Knole (that great house in Kent which I must take care not to go on about, because there are more pictures of it in my memory than of other houses of its kind) the staff in charge of its woods appear to have been more philosophical about their losses than I am able to be. They lost about 25 per cent of the park trees, which used once to create the illusion that the house still stood in a limitless expanse of dense woodland, pierced by grassy rides where parties of hunters might gallop in pursuit of the stag and the boar, and armed bands might lurk, debating how the substantial defences of the house might be penetrated.

In practical terms, no doubt, the National Trust was right afterwards to observe that most of the lost oaks and beeches at Knole were coming to the end of their days anyway, and to express greater concern about the problem of finding funds to repair the fences, smashed in a dozen places, which had kept Knole's deer from straying out onto the A 21 and falling under the wheels of the juggernauts trooping by.

Of course it was always another scene of artifice, the illusion fostered by carefully placed bands of woods concealing the crowded world beyond. It was not hunters' arrows, but flying golf-balls, that the walker had to be on his guard against, and the deer could tell an empty paper bag from one with a sandwich in at thirty yards' range. Indeed, the forest of the Weald had already been cut back almost to its present extent by the time the house was built. But now those evocative screens have been drastically thinned.

The trees were survivors of the foreign country of the past, and for us their successors will not be. King John is said to have hidden in an oak tree here from some over-mighty subject. The woods of Knole were part of the raw material from which Virginia Woolf spun the confection of *Orlando*. Lord Amherst, who first brought the gaudy Lady Amherst's Pheasant to Europe from China, where he was ambassador, kept his exotic birds in the park, in a Gothic folly, which the storm left straddled by a broadside of near misses from the oaks around it.

As I walked a few days after the storm among the prostrate brittle trunks of beeches under which we used to lay out the chicken salad for picnics, and where we had aimed our sledges down the steep bank which marked the course of a prehistoric stream, which used to flow into the Darent when one might have met mammoths in the woods, I could feel some of the sense of loss of personal acquaintances which grieved so many people so keenly on the morning after the storm.

Some of the very oldest trees had survived, ironically, because the storms they had ridden out long ago had brought down the boughs they had had in their prime, leaving them like gnarled fossils, still resolutely putting out a Beckettian leaf or two each spring. A row of very young oaks, mere puppies 20 or 30 years old, had been planted where the ground rose up towards the house, and seven out of twelve of them lay like dolls, as thoroughly destroyed as their mature elders.

Much of the mystery of Knole derives from the way it turns inwards, with its enclosed courtyards, its stern battlements, and the drawn curtains with which it keeps the intruding daylight from the precious tapestries and embroideries in its darkened rooms. A forbidding wall of Kentish ragstone excludes visitors from the private garden. According to the guidebook the garden is unremarkable, and it is probably more intriguing to explore the long perimeter and speculate on glimpses of what is within, like some adventurous intruder in a story by Walter de la Mare, than it would be to be invited in.

In the storm a row of a dozen oaks and beeches of the largest size fell onto the wall, crushing the masonry and forming a row of broad bridges up which one could stroll high into the air and look out over the forbidden demesne – a prospect of yet more splintered trees, and banks of rhododendrons now lying exposed to the winter. The row of great trunks tilted up against the wall resembled siege ladders, or the barrels of vast ordnance, trained on the house in an assault by giants.

Possibly it was along the crest of Sevenoaks Weald, on the greensand ridges across Ide Hill and Toys Hill, that the devastation of trees reached its extreme point. Whole plantations of privately and publicly owned wood-land were laid flat, or carved into avenues by the riotous inconsistencies of the gusts. Uniform young conifer plantings, not yet at their full strength, were simply obliterated in some places. It was as if the hem of some huge cloak had been dragged across the hills, snapping off the stalks of 20-foot trees as if they were tulip stems.

Again and again that characteristic prank of the 1987 storm was to be seen – the avenue cleared, as if by a supernatural bulldozer, through the middle of woods which remained virtually unscathed on either side. This phenomenon above all evoked an uncanny impression of a malicious or humorous will which took delight in showing off the modulations of its power. To some extent one could explain these variations away in terms of the domino principle – a few trees falling onto their neighbours and starting a successive pattern of collapse – or imagine that certain features on the ground had produced funnelling or sheltering effects. But the impression of a spontaneous, unmotivated destructiveness was intense and sometimes awe-inspiring.

Everywhere, too, the storm left that other characteristic mark of its passage – boughs where the leaves were shrivelled and blackened by salt carried in the wind. In Sussex, as in Brittany, summer turned to winter in a single night. Traces of the same salt were detectable as far inland as London, 40 miles downwind from the sea. The colour of the affected leaves was not like the natural shading of autumn; it reminded some observers of the clumps of dying leaves which had been the first signs of infection by Dutch Elm Disease a decade before: it was as if the wind had carried an instant infection with it.

The damage on Ide Hill at Emmetts House, a National Trust property, was among the worst. Emmetts was a botanical garden of the late 19th century, standing on the crest of the hill at the highest point in Kent, and skirted by woods which in the spring are famous for their bluebells and magnolias. In its Edwardian heyday, it employed twelve gardeners, and it had several considerable rarities among its trees, including a castor oil tree *Kalopanax pictus*, which had reached the unusual height of nearly 80 feet. By morning it was firewood.

At that elevation, shelter belts are essential to a botanical garden. Shelter belts and woods alike were beaten down with a savagery that had something wolfish about it. Carcasses of trees were piled up in heaps, not parallel but tossed arbitrarily this way and that. It was impossible to struggle through them or even to see where the footpaths to the bluebell valley had led. The few trees that still stood were almost more pitiable casualties than the fallen ones, because leaves, twigs and minor branches had been torn from them, leaving bare trunks covered with splintery white scars, so that they resembled trees struck by lightning and killed standing up. One was reminded of those stories of foxes which break into chicken-houses and embark on orgies of killing, far beyond anything they could possibly need for food. It seemed unnatural: but of course natural was the very thing it was.

CHAPTER 11

"WHOLE TREES IN MOTION"

"It is natural for a man to feel an aweful and religious terror when placed in the centre of a thick wood."

(John Evelyn, *Sylva*, 1670)

A tree is a process less unlike a storm than it might appear. Both are machines that depend on the strong impulse which impels molecules to stick together. Nature's abhorrence of a vacuum, which draws air thousands of miles to equalise disparities of pressure too slight for our senses even to perceive, also enables a tree to raise itself hundreds of feet above ground level.

Inside the tissue of a tree's trunk is a network of fine capillary tubes, reaching up continuously from roots to leaves. The molecules of water in the tubes cling to one another with such tenacity that the leaves are able to draw moisture and nourishment upwards simply by the suction induced by the evaporation of water from their exquisitely-adapted outer surfaces. Every tree is a machine for elevating a column of water high enough for it to overtop its neighbours. In summer a well-grown tree can draw up 300 gallons in a day. Then the evaporating water passes invisibly out into the air.

Of course a tree is a living, purposeful organism, while a storm simply happens, and soon exhausts itself. The parallels between them as physical processes might seem more apparent on the planet Jupiter, where the atmospheric conditions allow the vortex of a storm to persist for periods at least as long as the life of a tree. It is possible to speculate that in such conditions, evolution might have developed living, self-replicating weather-systems. Only familiarity makes the idea seem less likely than a living fountain of carbohydrate – for that is what a tree is, in the last analysis. What sort of temper would a live depression have, one wonders?

Like ourselves, the substance of a tree, apparently so massive, consists in the main of water derived from the soil and held in its necessary shape caught in a net of solid matter. One might assume that the solid matter of a tree was also from the soil, composed of the nutrient chemicals sucked up with the water through the roots. In fact the greater part of it – 90 per cent – comes not from the earth but from the air. Subtle chemical processes in the leaves draw in the carbon dioxide of the air and make carbohydrates with it – giving off oxygen as a waste product, which we scavenge when we breathe.

Properly considered, a tree is a structure which has made itself out of air. When a gale rampages through its branches, that is air thrashing against air. And when the parson at the funeral service tells us that we are dust, he makes too much of us altogether: nourished on leaves, or on animals which were nourished on leaves, we are air too. It goes without saying that once dead, we are buried in coffins of air – sawn, planed and polished.

Equipped with a mechanism for conjuring themselves into being out of next to nothing, trees have gone on to develop innumerable strategies for getting the better of their neighbours. They have had millions of years to elaborate them, some species drawn by selection into boldness, others into slow cunning. It is arguable that the subtlest of all trees is the beech.

The wind is one of the variables that all trees have to take into account. Some dig their heels in to resist it, some shoot up fast to get their business over before it can knock them down. In a storm, some fail as a whole or not at all, while some shed branches to save the trunk, as a lizard sheds its tail.

Deciduous trees are able to furl their sails like schooners when winter approaches. Conifers, by far the more ancient breed, keep their leaves, but have reduced them to thin needles. These are relatively inefficient as chemical workshops, but offer minimal resistance to the air. Deciduous trees can afford to spread their upper spars wide, pre-empting light and moisture from their neighbours, because they are normally leafless when rough weather comes. Conifers commonly grow with narrow tops, which can bend freely when the wind blows. In some conifer species, the upward growth is led by a single leading shoot, and if it is broken – as it often was in the storm – the tree can rise no further. This is why many forestry trees were rendered commercially valueless, even where they had survived with most of their height intact.

Not only species, but individuals, develop their own strategies for dealing with the stresses of the particular spot where they have taken root. A tree is very sensitive to the conditions in which it finds itself. It is a familiar thing that a tree will spread wide if has space round it, and will reach upwards in a forest where other trees compete for limited light, while providing shelter from the wind. On any exposed coast it is obvious how a tree's shape is moulded by the direction of the prevailing wind. Isolated trees which had learned to stand up for themselves fared better statistically than trees in woods during the storm.

The tactical faculties which an animal uses in prowling around for food are exerted by a tree in the way it grows. It reaches out into the shape that offers it the best prospect of survival. Its tribal and individual experience are displayed in the shape it has assumed. A writer on education once asserted rather grandly that all learning is "an arboriform stratification of guesses about the world". So it is: we can only extend our mastery from the points we have already reached, and only into areas that are not blocked off: we learn in the same way that a tree grows.

Experiments have shown that the sensibility of trees as they learn is very great. Where they need strength, there they put on strength. Saplings grown in absolutely still air will grow 30 per cent taller than others which are shaken by hand for only 30 seconds a day. According to the magazine *New Scientist* (21.1.88), there is even reason to believe that the growth of a plant can be affected just by being held briefly while it is being measured.

An Australian researcher called Max Jacobs grew pine trees in the 1930s and fixed guy ropes to support their trunks, so that only their upper parts could sway. The trees grew into a form resembling the spar of a ship, which is thickest where it needs to bear the most stress. The trunk thickened near the point of attachment to the guy ropes, while its lower parts and roots, with no work to do, developed so much more feebly than usual that the trees fell over as soon as the guy ropes were removed.

In the same way, stress on the roots makes for stronger roots. If the forces on the tree are constantly making the roots bend in a particular direction, they will often grow into an oval cross-section, broadest on the axis which resists the stress. The sitka spruce goes a stage further, and produces "waisted" roots with a figure-of-eight cross-section shaped almost like an architectural I-beam. Roots of this cross section are three times as resistant to bending as a rounded root of the same size would be.

In most of the casualties of the great gale, the crucial structural failure was in the root system. In *New Scientist*, Melvin Cannell and Mike Coutts, two Edinburgh researchers, have described their studies of damage to roots in trees which they winched over. They found that the roots on the windward side would stretch by 10 to 20 per cent before they began to snap, first at the outer edge of the root-plate, then closer in. On the leeward side, the roots were not stretched but compressed. This tended to make them bend, and the fate of the tree depended largely on how thick the roots were. The thicker they grew, the further from the trunk the point where they would buckle, and the less likely the tree was to fall.

The soil incorporated in the mass of roots can weigh as much as five tons, and its weight helps to keep the tree upright. But it is much less elastic than the roots, and begins to come loose long before they start to snap. As it grows looser, the tree is able to rock and disengage its roots still more. The soil is especially weak if it is wet. In 1987, the huge tree losses were partly due to the record rainfall suffered in many areas, which had thoroughly lubricated the soil around the bases of the trees.

While wood is growing, its inner structure comes to reflect the demands that are being made on it. On parts of a tree where compression forces apply (the underside of branches, for instance), the wood produces denser, more brittle fibres, good at resisting compression. Where the wood is under tension (along the top of branches, for instance) a less brittle fabric is produced, with a higher tensile strength.

Like a tuning fork, every tree tends to vibrate to its own natural frequency. A conifer about 45 feet tall has a natural twang of two or three seconds. As the wind thrusts it over, the tree stores up energy which it releases in springing back. A steady wind will heel a tree over, but will be less likely to damage it than irregular gusts, which allow it to spring back and gather momentum between one whiplash and the next. Repeated gusts in tune with the tree's frequency can set up a rhythm, in which the tree whips back and forth three or four times as far as a comparable steady wind would bend it. These rhythmic forces are similar to the amplified sway that a troop of soldiers can set up if they march in step across a suspension bridge – the reason for the old custom of breaking step as they cross.

Visualising this process of an amplified whiplash effect, it is possible to picture how it came about that some trees only yards apart were found the next day lying in exactly opposite directions: it was almost a matter of chance which point of the swing would eventually carry each one too far.

Within the categories of deciduous and coniferous trees, every species has a different blend of adaptations which have proved useful to its ancestors. The oak drives a massive tap root deep into the ground, broadens and strengthens its trunk, and seems to glory in its strength by retaining its leaves far into the winter as if contemptuous of anything the wind can do. But such a robust temperament requires ample moisture and a soil of a roast-beef-of-old-England richness to nourish it adequately. It can bear the loss of major branches without losing heart, and may survive for centuries, gradually declining into a gnarled bottle-shaped object more invulnerable to wind-throw than its descendants in their contemporary prime.

The Scots pine, which colonised Britain when the climate was still too harsh for the oak to gain a footing, can thrust down an even deeper tap-root – 20 feet in a sandy soil. The pines that failed in 1987 often had their trunks torn into a mass of splinters above ground, while their roots held firm. Once fallen, pine rots sooner than trees which put up far less of a fight.

The poplar puts less capital into survival. It hurries upwards like a rocket, and falls like the stick. Like its close relative, the aspen, it grows its leaves on long flexible stems,so that they flutter loosely in the wind and put minimal burden on the framework of the tree.

There is a relationship between the spread of a tree's branches and the spread of its roots (after ten million years, nothing is the way it is just by accident). A wide-spreading tree needs wide roots to gather moisture in the soil outside the "drip-line", where rainwater runs off its dome of leaves. In hastening for the sky, the poplar wastes no energy on breadth, and yields to the wind at the top like a spruce. Thus it avoids the need for wide roots: correspondingly, it has only a light grasp on the earth.

If a great storm comes every 100 years, generations of poplars have been and gone between one and the next: an oak designs itself to see out three or four, scattering acorns all the time. Whether oak or poplar has had the better fortune at the end of the game depends on many factors. The willow proved particularly vulnerable to the stresses of the night – strangely, considering its reputation for springiness. In Essex, a centre for the manufacture of cricket bats, 40 per cent of stocks were lost.

Without human intervention, practically the whole of England would be one immense woodland. After the glaciers melted 12,000 years ago, pines and birches spread across the land bridge from France and gradually recolonised the land again. The rate at which a forest can walk – more slowly than Birnam Wood on its way to Dunsinane – is reckoned to be 100 yards a year at the very most, as the trees spread into fresh territory.

They were followed, as the climate grew milder, by aspen, rowan and hazel, and later by oak, which can be shown by analysis of buried pollen to have forged northwards so fast that it had passed over the Pennines within a thousand years of its arrival. The other big broad-leaved species like elm, lime and beech (the last of these to spread in this era) followed before the land bridge disappeared, and Britain enjoyed several thousand years of weather warmer and wetter than today's. Towards the end of this period, men appeared and began to whittle the forests away again, as far as their stone axes and slash-and-burn agriculture allowed.

No doubt hurricanes struck at intervals in these vast stretches of time. The evidence of the pollen shows that extensive grassy glades often opened up in the prehistoric forest, where trees had fallen through old age or the assault of the wind. Then the woodland would mirror on a small scale the history of its original colonisation of the island. Lighter, faster-growing species would spring up, giving shelter for the slower growth of larger trees whose canopies would eventually inhibit the growth of their predecessors' descendants. Oak, lime and beech would reassert their dominance for a time until another catastrophe came round in the course of natural events.

From being one immense self-sustaining forest, England has become one of the most sparsely wooded countries in Europe. Even by the time of William the Conqueror, England had more grazing land and less woodland than Normandy. By Shakespeare's time, the clearances were so far advanced that it is said that there were fewer trees in the Lake District than there are today. Generations of exploitation have shaped and re-shaped the woodlands that survive, so that it is almost meaningless to talk about their primaeval character any longer.

For the most part, English woodland is almost as much an artefact as the manicured parklands of the 18th and 19th centuries. Trees would be cut back – coppiced – at different intervals according to species. The timber of each would be harvested at the point at which that particular timber was most useful, whether for wattles, or firewood, or medium-sized poles for domestic building. Some trees would be allowed to grow to full height before being felled to provide timber for major buildings or ships.

The system, a far more civilised procedure than the boring monocultures of much twentieth-century forestry, is now almost extinct, except in the case of chestnut. Only this species – a later arrival, probably introduced by the Romans – is still economic to manage in this way. But former coppiced woods are widespread. The system encouraged the development of extremely varied woodlands. Each species had its particular use, and pigs would forage for acorns and beechmast in the undergrowth. Paths were kept open, and creepers which tended to stunt growth were kept back. Coppiced trees will go on putting out new shoots almost indefinitely. It would have been a waste to allow trees to grow into senility, or to fall and rot as they must have done everywhere before men took control.

It was not a natural scene, in the strict sense. Man has a profound preference for seeing things tidy, and almost all our woodlands, whether active or former coppices, or managed for long-term timber, for shooting or for amenity, have long been worked over in accordance with current ideas of what is productive, or picturesque (an equally artificial concept). Dead trees, tangling undergrowth and inaccessibility are features of the unmanaged forest that a deep pioneering instinct itches to eliminate.

This fact lies behind one of the minor paradoxes of that instructive phenomenon, the public reaction to the storm. The very devastation which understandably gave such pain to most people who thought of themselves as nature lovers, and to landowners hard-hit in their pockets as well as in their territorial pride, evoked an incredulous quiet glee in another group, the researching naturalists. They saw in it a re-enactment of what must in the long perspectives of prehistoric time have been a recurrent convulsion, a regular factor in the natural economy of the forest before man's intervention. Where most of us saw only ruin, they saw the image of the primaeval wildwood partially re-created before their eyes.

However much it is tampered with, the character of woodland still reflects the character of the different species of trees, as they jockey for supremacy with greater or lesser ruthlessness. It depends on the soil, on moisture and on differences of a degree or two in average temperature. Oak, chestnut and lime are able to get along together to a considerable extent, except in situations which especially favour one species or another. But as centuries go by, the natural tendency of woodland is gradually to turn into beechwood, and to stay that way.

Oak was the broad-leaved tree which suffered the greatest loss in the storm in terms of volume. The weight of fallen timber was more or less equal for broad-leaved trees and for conifers (among which pines represented by far the largest tonnage). The actual number of conifers was by far the larger, of course, because there were so many plantations of young firs mown down in their millions. But among deciduous trees, oak accounted for about eight tons in every twenty tons of timber thrown to the ground.

The destruction of oaks was a great tragedy. Many great parks and private woodlands will show the scars for generations. Individual trees of heroic character were borne down after hundreds of years. But there was something even more terrible about the destruction of the beeches.

Beech is of a less tolerant disposition than other big trees. Like placid dinosaurs, the others do not greatly resent one another's presence. That is their weakness in the long run. Beech, with its bark as smooth as skin and its classical leaves, is perhaps "the most lovely of all forest trees", as Gilbert White claimed in The Natural History of Selborne. But it has a calculating spirit. From the time it first gains a footing in the complex vegetation of a developing wood, it works subtly and patiently to make it its monopoly if it can do so.

It does not need to do anything as crude as to attack its neighbours. It has time to spare. It spreads a dense canopy of those fine horizontal leaves to diminish the light reaching young trees that are trying to establish themselves below, and it deploys its roots with ingenuity to discourage rivals from ever getting a foothold at all. The peculiarly beautiful wax-like flow of its roots over the surface of the ground (or so close below it that rainfall soon exposes them) has an ulterior motive: it makes a shield against the penetration of alien seeds.

No need to take overt measures against the trees around it: in time they grow old and disappear, and the beech has made sure that its rivals have left no descendants. The haunting quality of a beechwood is based on the fact that it is exclusively a beechwood.

The observant writer Hugh Johnson puts it well in his *Encyclopaedia of Trees*: "An old beechwood has the longest echo of any woodland: a sound so eerie and disturbing that I remember it vividly from when I was a boy of four living on the chalk hills of Buckinghamshire. The beech thrives on lean chalk where other trees flag. In due course it takes it over completely; scarcely a bramble, barely a toadstool grow in the moss . . .Their layered canopy lets only threads of sunlight through. Hence the long answering echo: the echo of an empty room."

The beechwoods of the Weald were among its greatest glories. Nobly-grown individual trees were widespread, and on the chalky uplands, where the soil is shallow over the alkaline rock, there were extensive woods of just the kind Johnson describes. But the shallowness of the soil and the beech's sly habit of spreading its roots on the surface meant that they were the most vulnerable of all to an untypically strong gale. Beech also has the odd habit of producing beech mast, its nut-like packaged seeds, only in occasional years, known as "mast years". This year happened to be one of them. As if by prevision, the doomed trees had supplied the raw material for a new generation – but the considerable extra weight they had been carrying, along with their not-yet-fallen leaves, helped to make them even easier targets.

For every eight tons of oak that fell, seven tons of beech came down. Since it is a lighter tree, that implies that the number of individuals lost was at least as large.

But the land that the beech had claimed as its own was uniquely changed by the disaster. In breaking loose, the labyrinthine roots tore away the whole depth of the thin soil. The pewter-smooth trunks broke like glass as they struck the ground, so that trees which seemed at a distance to contain valuable straight timber proved at closer sight to be useless hulks criss-crossed with brittle fissures; internal stresses had created inward wounds which could not be seen. Beech does not last well on the ground: little of the fallen tonnage would ever be of any use, even where it was intact.

Cratered soil; useless timber carcasses. Where they had stood, no young saplings, no undergrowth, no bracken, no grass, no echo – nothing but the dead leaves of dead trees. There was no other kind of woodland where the night's ravages left such a complete emptiness.

CHAPTER 12

THE MILL ABLAZE

"Above 500 wind-mils over set and broken to pieces; or the Sails so blown round, that the Timbers and Wheels have heat and set the rest on fire, and so burnt them down . . . Three of the aforesaid belonging to one Jeremiah Fouldsham of Ely, a very Industrious man of mean Substance . . . to the almost Ruin and Impoverishment of the aforesaid Person."

(Daniel Defoe and A. Armiger of Ely: *The Storm*, 1704)

As more and more power and telephone lines were borne down by the millions of falling trees, more and more people found themselves enclosed in their own separate cells of emergency.

It was not whole areas that were cut off, as they seem to have been in Brittany. In France, local exchanges were put out of action by the power cuts. In Britain, local exchanges are equipped with batteries, or generators which cut in automatically if the power supply fails. Innumerable lines to individual houses broke down, but the basic system worked right through the power cuts, as it was designed to. The neighbour next door could often get a call through if one's own 'phone had gone dead. Police, ambulance and fire station phones continued to receive calls for help as fast as they could be answered – where they were not cut off themselves. In many private and public emergencies, this unpublicised feature of telephone design was of the greatest significance.

One line which carried an important call just before it was severed ran up the steep side of the South Downs above Brighton, to a house which stands between the Jack and Jill windmills. The mills, one black and the other white, are built on the very top of the Downs, in a position breezy enough to satisfy the most workaholic of millers. Apart from their value as landmarks, they constitute a unique epitome of mill design. There are two basic types of mill – the tower mill and the post mill – and Jack and Jill are the only historic mills in Britain which represent the two types standing side by side.

Mills are the first pieces of large scale automatic machinery that man ever devised. They are a contrivance evolved to an elaboration as efficient and fragile as the rigging of a ship – more fundamentally fragile than the upperworks of a tree, though incomparably less complex. In the last resort, of course, most of a mill's strength is borrowed from the strength developed by trees for their own purposes.

All the technology of the windmill revolves, literally, around the need for it to be able to turn to face the wind. If the wind is allowed to catch a mill's sails obliquely, it can easily overturn the whole construction, however massive its timbers may be. Jack, the tower mill, has a wooden "beehive" cap on top of its brick tower, with a spinning tail like that of a helicopter, ingeniously arranged to turn the cap and keep the sails facing the wind automatically.

Jill is smaller, and built mostly of wood. It is not just the cap that turns, but the main structure of the mill, 43 feet tall and weighing three tons. A similar fantail behind, built onto the steps by which one enters this rotating structure, aims it at the wind, as a weathercock is aimed by its tail. When the mill is not grinding corn, a powerful iron brake stops the sails moving. The brake clamps onto the circumference of a timber wheel six feet or more across, which turns on the axis of the sails. The working area of each sail, or sweep, consists of shutters arranged like Venetian blinds, so that they can be turned edgewise to the wind when not in use, by remote control.

Jack lost her guts years ago (one is supposed to call mills "she", like ships, even if they have a name like Jack). But Jill still had much of her machinery, and a preservation trust had just managed to bring her back into working order after 13 years' work – much of it achieved by its members' own sweat.

The whole purpose of a mill is to catch wind. On the night of the storm, Jack and Jill caught a handful. Deep in the night, in the house between the mills, Vera Deering woke her husband Bob, Jack's owner. She was worried by the uproar, and asked him to look round. He peered out of the window, and saw what looked like a comet, scattering a peacock's tail of sparks towards him through the darkness.

"Jill's on fire!", he said, and reached for the telephone. He rang Simon Potter, a member of the preservation society, who lives at the bottom of the hill, in Clayton village.

"I grabbed a torch, pulled on the first clothes I could reach – my best shirt and odd socks – and 'phoned two other members who live nearby", says Mr Potter. "The lane was blocked by trees in both directions, so there was no hope of using the car. The only thing was to walk, and I set off up the hill. It was so dark that I could only see 30 yards ahead. I had no chance of finding the path – I just went upwards. I knew the mills were above me, but I couldn't see them.

"Several times I was blown clean off my feet by the wind. Halfway up, I passed something lying on the grass, and realised it was one of the blades from Jill's fantail. It had been carried 200 yards; those things weigh about a hundredweight each. Then I began to see the stream of sparks in the sky ahead of me.

"The wind must have been blowing about 120 mph. Near the top it was impossible to stand upright, and I was forced to crawl the last 50 yards on my knees. I came up to the mill from the side in case anything else blew off it. The noise was deafening. I fought my way against the gale and up the steps. But at the top of the steps I found a gap three feet wide between me and the mill door."

The three-ton mill must have been pushed bodily backwards, thrusting the fantail structure back too, steps and all. Then it had righted itself, breaking away from the fantail in coming upright again.

"The door is about 20 feet above ground. I had to undo the padlock and then stretch across to get in. The mill was pitch dark and full of smoke inside, and swaying backwards and forwards like a boat at sea. I rushed up, finding my way by instinct . The sweeps were turning despite the brake-wheel being chocked and the brake-lever pegged. The friction between the brake-wheel and the brake shoe was making the smoke."

"I released the brake to take off the friction, and the sweeps began spinning freely. I worked out that they were going round at about 30 to 35 revolutions a minute".

The sweeps are not designed to turn at more than a fraction of this speed. In the normal way, a miller would be worried if they were turning 15 or 16 times in a minute. Each sweep is about 30 feet from hub to tip, so that the tips must by now have been moving at speeds above 65 mph, putting the structure under immense stress. If it had not been for the ten-year restoration effort, in which 70 per cent of the mill's timbers had been replaced, it might have been shaken to pieces at this moment.

"We keep a bucket of ashes in the mill for just such an emergency. The ashes are meant to give extra friction between the wheel and the shoe. Robert Deering had come from the house and joined me, and we applied some ash and lowered the brake. There was a noise like a train trying to stop in an emergency, a screeching of metal on wood. Sparks flew in all directions – it looked like a Catherine wheel. But the sweeps showed no sign of stopping.

"We rushed outside and scooped up buckets of gravel. Other friends were making their way up the hill to help us by now. At this point we noticed a glow from the front corner of the mill. The sparks from the brake had set the body of the mill on fire!"

Potter grabbed a fire extinguisher and pushed the plunger – but only a trickle came out. A human chain was formed, passing buckets of water along from the house, about 40 yards away. Those who could face the airy gap between steps and millhouse went up to work at the brake and throw the water as near to the flames as they could.

"The fire was coming from the top chamber, and we could not get in to it until the sweeps had been brought under control. We could only chuck water in the general direction the flames were coming from.

"It took two hours before we managed to stop the sweeps, throwing water down inside the mill all the time. Then we could pour water onto the glowing timbers from outside, and put the fire out."

Black to the eyebrows, the best shirt irretrievably ruined, Potter and his weary helpers paused in the dawn to take stock. The sparks from the wheel had left a line of deep burns in the floorboards, and most of the three-inch wooden rim of the wheel had been burnt out. When the body of the mill had lurched backwards and dislodged the fantail, the whole structure

The storm clouds from 180 miles above: a satellite's infra-red photograph, taken at
5.42 am, in which the drier air of the jetstreak shows up darker than the cold-
topped clouds over the North Sea, and the cooler air drawn in from the west. The
jetstreak's tattered right-hand edge indicates strong shearing forces between fast-
and slow-moving air.

The pine forest of Broceliande in Brittany before the night of October 15 (chapter three).

The trees of Broceliande snapped and tattered by the force of the storm.

Near Quimper, Brittany, amphibious vehicles clear floods caused by fallen trees blocking watercourses.

Pierre Pelliat, a farmer at Châteaulin, Brittany, surveys a ruined field of maize.

Route Orange, west Jersey, with its handsome avenue of ageing pines, objects of local controversy over how they should be replaced (page 34).

A dilemma brutally resolved: the same spot on Route Orange after the gale.

A branch plunges through Mrs Millie Le Clercq's ceiling in Le Hocq, Jersey.

The anemogram that traces the rise and fall of the wind across Guernsey.

The roof of the Mayfair Hotel, Jersey, torn away in shreds (page 35).

At North Beach, Guernsey, owner-builder Robert Whalley found his new catamaran Talatasha *dismasted and thrown upside down on top of another yacht.*

Shattered windows reflect the damage in the ravaged Steers Restaurant on Worthing Sea Front.

Brighton Pavilion half-buried in the ruins of its famous elms, and encased in the builders' cladding which dislodged one of its pinnacles (page 44).

The stone finial which plunged through the floor of the Pavilion's Music Room.

Winching the two-ton finial from its crater in the £90,000 carpet.

Roofs stripped of tiles, and brick walls sucked out by the wind, on the Promenade at Peacehaven (pages 55–56). The house on the right, with the garage at the back, was so badly damaged that it had to be demolished.

Modern and traditional roofs stripped away at a farm near Henfield, Sussex, with cars and a speedboat damaged by flying debris.

In a sea of broken glass, Marge Ostle and Celia Inman inspect the wreck of their livelihood at Sidlesham Glasshouses near Brighton: ruined crops of courgettes and seedling lettuces.

A van tossed on its side and ripped open by the gale in St Catherine's Terrace, Hove Sussex.

Some of the 200 caravans torn to pieces by the wind at Peacehaven, while their occupants fled in pyjamas: Rushy Hill Site.

Grace O'Connor, a caravan refugee, with her dog Teddy.

Ann and Clare Cooper shelter in a car at a wrecked Peacehaven van site.

Caravans capsized and flung on top of one another at Seaford on the Sussex coast (pages 57–61).

The 93-year-old Shanklin Pier, Isle of Wight, has its central section, where the theatre stood, swept away (pages 153, 186).

Steven Thomas surveys the wreckage at the Robert de Mortain, Hastings (page 63).

Daylight shows where a four-ton chimney fell through four storeys of the Queen's Hotel, Hastings, killing Mr Ronald Davies (page 64).

Roots rear up from underground among the tombstones in the churchyard of Holy Cross Church, Uckfield, Sussex.

Another tree which fell near Uckfield Church, bringing a wall of flints down.

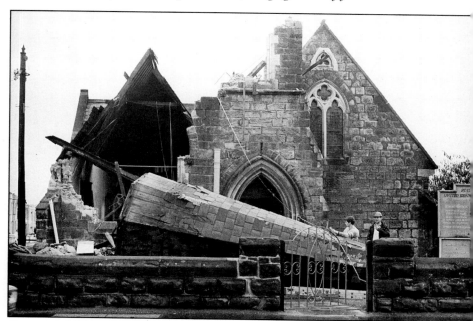

Removing the spire of St Luke's United Reform Church, St Leonards, from the side-aisle where it had fallen (page 61).

Yachts toppled onto their sides by the wind at Thorpe Bay, Essex.

A wooden annexe squeezed out of shape like a cardboard carton, at Uckfield Church of England School.

Park Avenue, Orpington, blocked six times in 50 yards: one car pinned down.

Bow-saws could not hope to make much impression on the row of large trees which barred Chesswood Road, Worthing.

A many-trunked cedar of Lebanon bursts through the pavement in the Library Gardens, Leigh-on-Sea, Essex.

The oaks of Sevenoaks: six lost out of the row of seven planted beside the Vine cricket ground (page 71).

The caprice of the wind: the leeward side of the avenue at Beechmont's Farm, near Sevenoaks, is obliterated (page 66).

At Riverhill, near Sevenoaks, trees blocking the road have been lopped to clear the route, but a giant beech in the field lies untouched.

Under a straddling bombardment of trees, the Bird House at Knole somehow survives unscathed.

Amputated boughs and fallen trunks litter a picnic site beside the moat at Leeds Castle, Kent.

Aerial view of Scotney Castle, with an uprooted cedar leaning on its neighbour to make a precarious bridge over the drive (page 204).

*A collapsed traditional Sussex flint
wall in Southfield Road, Eastbourne.*

*Damaged power lines at Horsted
Keynes, Sussex*

A smashed wall at Redington Road, Hampstead, London

Builders' hoardings torn down beside the National Gallery in Trafalgar Square, central London.

Festival Hall, South Bank, London.

One of the crushed cars in London.

In deepest Belgravia: untamed jungle rampant among the consulates in Eaton Square, London.

The sculptor Antony Gormley in the ruins of his Brixton studio (page 170).

"In Memory of the Fallen": the War Memorial on Islington Green, London, acquires a double meaning overnight (page 140).

St Thomas à Becket's damaged statue beside St Paul's Cathedral (page 140).

The collapsed roof of the medieval Waxham Great Barn in Norfolk (page 146).

This caravan from a clifftop site at East Runton, Norfolk, was blown over the cliff and down to the beach below.

Frances Esposito with baby Petr, and Margaret Dale with her makeshift listening tube (page 168).

Cessna light aircraft at Shoreham airport, Sussex, flipped onto their backs and thrown against one another by the wind. There were similar scenes at Biggin Hill, Brighton, Margate and Southend airports.

The Sealink ferry Hengist, *torn from her moorings at Folkestone and driven ashore and holed on the Warren bank, with 22 on board (page 154).*

The 5.25 from Swansea, which crashed from a broken bridge into the River Tywi in Wales on October 19. The front carriage, in which three passengers and the driver died, is almost submerged in the swollen river (page 178).

This tree blocking the double railway track at Crawley, Sussex, was one of about 7,000 which came down on lines in the south-east.

In Kew Gardens, the Tree of Heaven planted in 1837 sprawls across the William IV Temple, built in the same year (page 206).

Dame Jennifer Jenkins, Chairman of the National Trust, visits storm-damaged gardens in Kent and Sussex after the storm.

Clive Farrell, of the Sion House Butterfly Centre, examines a returned fugitive, a Brazilian Owl (page 193).

Charlotte, Rosie and Matthew Woodward, of South Chailey, Sussex, while away a two-week power cut with woollies, scarves and Scrabble.

Reduced to firewood: disposing of casualties in the garden designed by Capability Brown at Sheffield Park, Sussex (page 204).

Heavy Ardennes horses at Sydenham Hill Wood, near Dulwich, London, clearing timber from ground too rough for tractors.

jammed, and could no longer turn to face the wind. Until the fantail could be repaired, wire stays would have to be fitted to stop the mill falling onto its side if a strong wind came from any other direction.

Repairs looked like being an 18-month job. Even doing as much of the work as possible themselves, the cost to the society would be £5,000. Considering what the damage might have been, they thought the night's work cheap at the price.

"It was about this time that someone tried the 'phone and found it was dead", says Potter. "If it had failed just a little earlier, the mill would have burned down, and we would not even have known about it."

The official emergency services were having their communication problems too. As it happened, local services were already on special alert over much of the area, because the incessant rain had brought the Darent and other rivers to the point of overflowing. The Southern Water Authority was sending regular reports to the police, and the police were passing the information on to council officers like Harry Binks, deputy emergency planning officer for Kent, on duty that night.

"In the early hours the flood messages began saying: 'Yes, but there are other things happening as well' ", Eric Wilcock, the senior emergency planning officer, explains. "Harry rang me between four and four-thirty. My lights had gone, and I was managing with candles, but luckily my 'phone was still working. By five we had realised that we had a major problem on our hands, and we activated our county emergency plan."

But as one emergency turned into another, communication became increasingly fragile. The men on the spot began to find themselves as much preoccupied with survival as with reporting to headquarters. Sussex ambulance service became unable to answer distress calls when its 200-foot radio transmitter mast came down. The radio mast on the police station at Worthing was put out of action in the same way, and the cars and foot patrol officers under its control were cut off just as the number of calls for help (which now included reports of looting) started to mount.

A Sevenoaks police car was driving through the Otford area on the lookout for flooding just as the wind began to rise to extraordinary levels. "It was like World War Three", Chief Inspector Mick Lofthouse told Bob Ogley, editor of the *Sevenoaks Chronicle*, who wrote the earliest history of the night, *In the Wake of the Hurricane*. "Trees were crashing down all round us, and I didn't think we would make it back to the station."

Electricity began to flash between wildly swinging thousand-volt power cables, reminding the two officers of "a science fiction film or an invasion from Mars". They tried to get back to their base, but a tree fell in front of them, and as they turned the car round, another fell just behind. They abandoned the trapped car and scrambled on foot through a sea of fallen branches back to Sevenoaks police station, where the chief inspector decided to call all his cars off the road, rather than risk having them all similarly immobilised.

Fire brigades were under such a torrent of alarm calls that they had to make hard choices in concentrating their efforts on the most serious. "In 25 years I have never seen anything like it", David Drew-Bear, divisonal officer in the East Sussex brigade, said next day. "It was utter devastation. Between 2 am and 10.30 am we received more than 400 calls – more than 30 concerning people trapped in buildings. People got quite irate, not realising how widespread the damage was, when we tried to clear the lines."

In the towns, the firemen and the police could move around without too much difficulty. In Brighton and elsewhere special patrols were sent out to shopping areas where looters were reported to have been active. In Bexhill, firemen rescued a vicar and his wife trapped by a chimney which fell in their bedroom. In Brighton, a 21-year-old student called Warren Lynch was trapped in his bed, pinned down with suspected broken legs, after a chimney came down in his flat at 3.30 am. Firemen worked for four hours to free him, using jacks. But outside the towns, there was little that could be done about the looting reports, and it was touch and go how long victims of the storm might have to wait for rescue.

A husband near Rye set out to drive his wife to hospital after she was taken ill. Near the village of Beckley the car was trapped by trees, and the husband found a telephone and called the police to ask for help, because his wife was "turning blue". An ambulance set out from Rye, but it too was stranded just outside the town, and had to give up. The unfortunate couple were marooned until daylight; luckily the wife recovered.

William Bennister in Rottingdean was not so lucky. A man in his sixties, he went out at the height of the storm to try to prevent his garage door being torn away. But the effort was too much for him, and he collapsed. His wife Doreen found him slumped on the ground and called the ambulance. The ambulance could not get through, and she ran to the house of a doctor not far away. But Mr Bennister proved to be already dead.

Hardly any traffic was venturing onto the roads by now. At Detling Hill, near Maidstone, Kent, James Puddephat, from Berkshire, was driving through the uproar with his wife. Suddenly he complained of chest pains, and she pulled on the handbrake while he collapsed with a heart attack. He was dead before he could be got to hospital. In Liverpool, a motorcyclist called James McCollum was killed when a gust blew his bike into the central reservation of the M62.

Martin Jones, of Heathfield, Sussex (father of 8-year-old Matthew who had foretold a hurricane that morning) was called out at about 4 am to deal with an electrical fault at a factory 18 miles from Heathfield. He had not got far when a tree fell on his car.

"You imagine you'd see a tree if it's coming down on you, but I never did. The car just suddenly stopped, with the tree right across the back seat. It was a write-off. There were some more trees which looked unsafe, so I got away quickly, and found a 'phone box to shelter in. It was rocking around, but it was still working, and I called home."

He roused his wife, Paula, who persuaded a neighbour to drive out to fetch him. "Matthew was woken up by all the excitement, and he said: 'I told you so', which was most irritating", says Paula Jones.

The meteorologist himself was not awestruck or abashed when he realised how much trouble he had started: "I'm not specially interested in the weather, but I was waiting to go to school that morning, and I picked up the weather book I had been given for Christmas. I was comparing the pictures with the clouds outside the window, and I thought they looked alike. Everyone just laughed at me, so when I saw there really was a storm, I was glad."

Probably the most imperturbable of the night's motorists was Douglas Nye, motoring correspondent of *The Observer*. He had an article to write at his home in Farnham, Surrey. As journalists do, he had put it off to the very last moment for catching his deadline for next Sunday's paper, and he sat up after midnight cheerfully typing away, watching videos of comedy programmes out of the corner of his eye, and hardly aware of sounds of rising tumult outside.

"The piece was required first thing next morning", he wrote later in a memorable *Observer* piece, itself no doubt rushed to the office with comparable urgency. It does not seem to have occurred to him to telephone his copy: it would be unfair to suggest that he found the prospect of driving through the gale of the century simply too tempting to miss.

"The nocturnal whizz up the M3 from Farnham is usually quick and easy, free of 'phone and family – a chance to sit and think, perhaps just sit", he explained. "Around 2 am, copy finished, I walked to our brand-new (200 miles only) Renault 21 Savanna. I remember thinking: 'Mmm . . . bit breezy tonight', but nothing penetrated as too unusual".

It was pitch black, with flurries of rain. "I first appreciated the storm's severity when a sustained cannonade of twigs and leaves heaved the Savanna broadside and smeared sap across its screen. Puddles beaten by the gale were misting into the air, like the sea under a chopper's downwash . . .

"On the narrow tree-lined roads before the motorway, I fully realised the danger from bending trunks and flying boughs. I clicked my seat forwards to increase upward vision through the screen – gawping up at the flailing trees as much as forward at the road.

"Interesting choice: what speed ? Slow enough to stop if you spot a toppler ? Or quick enough to spend *the least possible time* in the danger zone?

"I opted to run well clear of the windward-side at around 40 mph. At that speed, if I stayed in third or fourth gear to keep instant acceleration, I'd at least have the option either to brake or Boot It."

Once he reached the motorway, he felt safer, in spite of debris tumbling across it, as he was "literally blown into central London" on the skirts of a following wind.

Less daring motorists were forced out onto the roads by necessity. As the gale reached its peak, several expectant mothers began to feel the first warnings of labour. It would be an interesting subject for a paper in the

British Medical Journal to analyse whether these terrifying night events tended to set labour in motion or, conceivably, to inhibit it – which is the alternative one might expect natural selection to have favoured.

Julie Pell was one of these mothers. As her labour pains became unmistakeable, at about 2.30 am, she and her husband John set off to drive from Cowden, near Tunbridge Wells, to the maternity hospital at Pembury, ten miles away. But the storm played the same trick on them as it had played on the Sevenoaks policemen. Leaving their car trapped by a tree ahead and a tree astern, they battled their way home on foot.

Mrs Pell was in the second stage of labour by the time they got there, but luckily the telephone was still working, and the health services were able to contact a doctor in Edenbridge, five miles away, who set out on a cross-country trek not unlike their own to reach them.

Marilyn Price of Blackham, Kent, set out to hospital by car at just about the same time, and her way too was blocked by fallen trees. Her labour was less straightforward: the authorities at Pembury Hospital, still in touch by telephone, grew concerned, and made inquiries to see whether a helicopter might be able to fly on such a wild night, and bring her in to the hospital.

Even in a place the size of Bexhill-on-Sea, a clear run to the maternity hospital was no longer guaranteed. Mrs Elizabeth Elliott-Noye was woken by the storm at 3.30 am, and lay thinking what an awful night it would be to have a baby, and telling herself that the pains she was feeling were just imagination. When they started coming every ten minutes she gave up the imagination hypothesis and woke her husband Bill.

He rang Eastbourne Hospital, where they were booked, and the hospital told them to come over. But it advised them to check with the police first, as the weather was "quite bad". The police said that trees were down on all three roads between Bexhill and Eastbourne, and that they had better stay where they were for the time being. The Elliott-Noyes went back to timing the contractions, which were growing increasingly painful, and took what comfort they could from the knowledge that the ambulance station was only five minutes away.

Frances Esposito, in the village of Ardingley, near Haywards Heath, was woken up at 3 am when her six-year-old eldest son came into the bedroom crying. "He was frightened because the lights had gone out, and he had to be comforted and put back to bed. I heard our next-door neighbour's greenhouse fly away and crash down not very far from our window.

"I pottered around for a bit, and heard our greenhouse shatter into a thousand pieces, but I didn't think too much of it, mainly because we had had a very bad wind a few weeks before, and I just thought 'Here we go again'. But I think that must have been what started me off in labour."

She went to bed again and slept till half past six. Meanwhile the unseen and unceasing cascade of trees out in the darkness, blocking all roads out of the village and severing one telephone line after another, gradually cut Ardingley off from the outside world altogether.

CHAPTER 13

LONDON IN THE DARK

*"All the morning a grievous and blustery wind: the devill
appeared at Westminster [and] Whitehall and frightened the
gards out of their wits."*
(Anthony Wood: *Journal*, September 17, 1666)

All over London, sleepers were waking up. Dougal Gonsal, chief engineer of the London Borough of Camden, stirred in bed at the sound of the gale and wondered drowsily what was happening to Hawkridge, a tower block in his charge, recently emptied of tenants because of doubts about its construction.

Duncan Donald, curator of the Chelsea Physic Garden, that secret enclosure by the Thames which seemed to have closed itself off with a curtain of foliage from the hubbub of the city, was more abruptly woken by the descent of a large botanical rarity through his roof.

David Wood and his wife Christine woke in stark terror, as the outer wall panels of their thirteenth-floor flat in Stockwell were torn away and they found themselves struggling to avoid being "sucked out into the air" by the vacuum effect of the gusts. Two hundred other tenants of the 16-storey block were hastily evacuated, and Mrs Wood was taken to hospital suffering from severe shock.

Whether Terence Leo Marrin ever woke up to the hissing of the boughs cannot be known: dossing out in Lincoln's Inn Fields under one of those ancient plane trees which have rustic bird boxes nailed all over them, he was killed when the tree fell and crushed his skull. He was a man of 65, born in County Durham, so much alone in the world that the police were never able to trace any next-of-kin, and the council bore the cost of his funeral. Thomas Maher, sleeping in the same sheltered patch, escaped unhurt, and woke to find his friend dead beside him.

Antony Gormley, a young sculptor living in Peckham, woke up worrying about the new studio into which he was about to move his work. At about 3 am he pulled on some clothes and went round the corner to see that the studio was all right. He secured a strip of loose roofing material, and went back to bed reassured.

The Doke family, not far away in Catford, began to get up at just about the time that Gormley was going back to bed. But it was not the wind that woke them: in fact, they scarcely worried about it as they dressed and collected their baggage, ready to catch an early morning flight to a holiday in Spain from Gatwick airport. John Doke's brother Robert had promised to drive the four of them to the airport.

Thousands of Londoners lay trying to disentangle dream from fact in a mixture of sounds that seemed to fit in with no customary set of circumstances. Afterwards it was difficult to agree on just what elements made up the experience, for it was so difficult to compare it with any previous one. For some, it was the majestic steadiness of the wind which impressed itself on the imagination; for others, its wayward feints and pounces.

My wife Caroline recalls that it echoed between the houses lining our north London street, with a deep resonant "Hoo! hoo!" I cannot particularly call any such sound to mind, but was struck with the incessant clatter of dustbins, tin cans and assorted debris being rolled along the street, as if some insanely persistent person was trying to provoke the whole neighbourhood, and intent on keeping it up all night. The trees with their full foliage seemed to have been combed into simplified rounded shapes by the hardly faltering pressure from one side.

Thousands must, like us, have turned blearily out of bed to see what was happening, blinked at the barometer with a sense that there must surely be some mistake, and climbed to the highest point of the house to look out with incredulity at a spectacle not seen since the days of the wartime blackout: the whole immense city laid out in the darkness of a universal power cut, with no more electric light visible than the red beacons flashing on top of the Post Office Tower, powered by their own emergency generators, and the lurid flickering of headlights and blue police car lamps, glimmering in the canyons of the streets.

As a matter of curiosity, it was not so very dark. For once one could see the dense blanket of cloud overhead untinted by that amber glare – reflected back from sodium street lamps – which makes London an unrewarding place for astronomers, and normally makes it visible from the country twenty miles off, like a sullen conflagration on the horizon. The clouds were relatively featureless, and gave no strong impression of rapid motion. But they let through enough light for the modelling of buildings to be made out, and one could have made some shift to jostle through the gusts and find one's way along the litter-strewn streets. The cloud cover was low, but intermittent: other observers recall bright moonlight at the height of the gale.

Heathrow airport is always closed to flights in the middle of the night, because the area round it is so densely populated. (Gatwick operates under no such restriction, but had to close for an hour between 5 am and 6 am, because the wind blew obliquely across its single runway). So it is probable that there was no one in the air looking down on London at the moment the the lights went out at 4.25 am – no sleepy passenger peering down at that most exquisite signal of human habitation, the woven skeins of lights wandering to the horizon across a great city – and then startled to see the entire display disappear in an instant. For the lights went out over the south-east not patchily through piecemeal failures, but all together, in response to one conscious decision.

Lord Marshall, chairman of the Central Electricity Generating Board, was another of those who were woken up early. He was roused by his telephone from a dreamless sleep at 5 am. We know that it was a dreamless sleep, because he is on record as declaring that he never dreams and never has nightmares.

But the call that roused him alerted him to a situation which had some of the characteristics of nightmare. He had given a standing order that he was to be told at once whenever there was a major operational crisis in his industry. The CEGB is the owner of Britain's nuclear power stations, so that the possibilities raised by a night-time call include nightmare on the very largest scale.

Those firework displays of electricity springing from cable to cable on power lines, which have sometimes figured as a lurid background to scenes in earlier chapters, were a phenomenon which could have led to a far wider disaster than the anecdotal events that they illuminated. The great power cut of 1987, which pulled the plugs on one-sixth of the entire power requirement of England and Wales, was a necessity forced on the CEGB as a lesser evil than the alternative.

When they turned out the lights, the breakfast-time peak of demand was scarcely two hours away. When the call went through to Lord Marshall, half an hour later, the position was still deteriorating. But it is fair to assume that as he hastily rose and got ready for an early appearance at the National Grid control headquarters, Lord Marshall was chortling. By disposition and physiognomy, he is a man marked out by nature to gobble when things go wrong and chortle when things go right – and also to see a godsend when presented with one, even when it is thickly disguised.

An event on the scale of the storm is bound to become a political event. If it had shown up major shortcomings in emergency arrangements of any kind, a scandal would have been declared and heads would have rolled. It could potentially have become yet another stick – and a powerful one – for the Government to beat local government with. It will undoubtedly affect important political debates about agriculture, forestry and conservation in the years ahead. But the point at which it might have brought about an almost immediate major shift in a central area of Government policy was in its impact on power supply.

Electricity is the only source of power which we have no means of storing. The electricity which sets the filament glowing in a light bulb when we turn it on has been manufactured and delivered between the instant when we turn the switch, and the instant – imperceptibly later – when the power warms the wire and makes it glow. It travels as fast as light, and fades as suddenly as a shadow falls.

Except by indirect means, there is no way one can store up a surplus to keep in hand to cover any fluctuations in demand. If there is no use for the output of a power station, it has to be turned off – and it can be a slow and costly business getting it going again. Demand over Britain as a whole can fall to 20 million kilowatts at night, and rise to a peak of nearly 50 million kilowatts at the morning and evening peaks.

Electricity is also expensive to make. The cost of providing it depends on how successfully the operators run a balancing act between over-provision and under-provision, bearing in mind that some kinds of power station cost more to run than others. In the north and in Scotland, there is normally an excess of generating capacity over demand. In the south, there can be a shortfall, but a cross-Channel link allows Britain to draw on the output of the big nuclear power stations in France, as well as the surplus from the north.

The power lines of the National Grid link supply and demand over Britain as a whole, enabling the CEGB, owner of the power stations and the Grid, to run them in one vast co-ordinated operation. It can summon into action the exact combination of generating stations which can meet demand most economically. Its customers are the area electricity boards, and their customers are ourselves.

In the general election four months before, the Conservatives had been returned to power with a manifesto which included a commitment to privatise the power industry. A competitive structure would improve efficiency and quality of service, it was argued. After the disappointing results of the privatisation of telephones and gas, the Government was determined to avoid setting up another privatised monopoly which would be under no more incentive to be competitive than the public utility it replaced. The CEGB was to be broken up.

Lord Marshall argued, with a rumbustuous insistence indiscreet in a public servant, that a break-up would destroy all the qualities of co-ordination which enabled it to supply a more reliable service on a smaller margin than any other system of its kind. Now, at the very time when the Government was considering its decision, the chance had come to show how it could cope with the biggest crisis it had ever faced.

The high voltage cables of the National Grid carry many times the current of the local lines used by the area boards to carry power to villages, factories and households. If the Grid's lines are damaged, they are very dangerous and costly to repair. So they are massively built, with automatic cut-out mechanisms to prevent damage if there is a breakage, or if current begins to jump from cable to cable.

Current was jumping from cable to cable everywhere that night. Most of the showers of sparks making pyrotechnics throughout southern England were from lesser cables, but some were from the Grid. The alarm was raised at 4 am in the Grid's headquarters beside Southwark Bridge, when the lines from Dungeness "tripped" and automatically cut out. The link to France cut out soon afterwards.

Nuclear power stations like Dungeness 'A' and the French stations are costly to build but cheap to run, so they are run day and night to recover their capital costs. They were supplying a large part of total output at that quiet time of the night. The technicians juggled the switches to find alternative routes and bring in other stations, but more lines were tripping faster than they could do so. As stations became cut off from the network, they had to be closed down, because there was nowhere for their electricity to go. Littlebrook, Isle of Grain, Tilbury, West Thurrock and Kingsnorth were all lost one after another.

At 4.25 am the loss of power stations forced the CEGB to black out the two huge ring mains, with voltages of 400,000 and 275,000 volts, which supply London and its 1.7 million consumer households.

But power stations normally use electricity to start up again. There was none to be had. There was a danger of a vicious circle, leading to the progressive breakdown of the whole National Grid. It has happened in other countries. The breakfast peak was only two hours away, and the Government was watching.

The penalties of failure in this nationwide juggling act would have been high. In 1965 and again in 1977, the whole of New York was plunged into prolonged blackouts, after relatively minor defects had caused progressive overloading and cutting out of the system. Engineers struggling to correct the faults with incomplete information only made things worse. In 1965 it took more than 24 hours to reconnect supplies, and the electricity company had to pay millions of dollars' worth of compensation. In 1977 an instant carnival of looting began as the lights went out. At one Bronx car showroom, 50 cars were driven out through the doors. Some 7,000 arrests were made that night, and 400 police were injured. The overall financial losses were eventually estimated to have been no less than $310 million (£200 million).

When the wind finally began to drop, the technicians in the CEGB's control room found with relief that the automatic cut-outs had at least prevented widespread permanent damage. Orders were given to try a "black station start" at three of the lost stations, Kingsnorth, Grain and Littlebrook. Battery-powered emergency generators started diesel motors, which in turn started the generating turbines, without any need for outside power. By ringing the changes to find usable lines, their current was passed out into the network. While London was kept in the dark, it was fed to other power stations so that they could start up in their turn.

By 8.30 am most of them were working; by 10.30 am bulk supplies were being fed to all the area boards again, and helicopters were out making visual checks on the pylon lines to see where they had been damaged. The area boards were able to restore supplies to London almost at once, because 90 per cent of their cables there run underground. It was weeks in some cases before they could fully reconnect the lighter-weight networks that take supplies to every village and farmhouse in the south. But as far as the CEGB was concerned, the night had been a famous victory.

"It was quite something. Everybody has been congratulating me on my influence with the Almighty for laying on the hurricane as a demonstration of our efficiency", Lord Marshall said soon afterwards, with a chortle meant to resound from St Paul's to Whitehall. It was just the kind of crisis which can tip the balance for a Government hesitating between two courses of action.

In a great city, the story of a great natural disaster is apt to turn into a story about administration. It may be prosaic, but if the administrative arrangements failed, there would be more drama than anyone would like to see. By now, the county and district councils out in the wind-battered shires had put their emergency plans into operation. As for London, it had ceased to be a unit of local government with the abolition of the Greater London Council, but it still had an emergency plan. Each of the 32 boroughs has its own arrangements, based on its resources and special needs, and a systematic call-out system for workers. They are triggered by requests for help from the police.

There is an all-London plan, too. It would have treated the great storm not as a storm but as a flood – as it would treat any other major catastrophe, from an earthquake to a jumbo jet crashing in Oxford Street in rush hour.

In the days when the Thames Barrier was not yet built, and tidal floods were a real threat, the boroughs were organised into five groups so that riverside boroughs were linked with others which were in no danger. The aim was to ensure that emergency help could be brought to bear quickly. The GLC took no active role unless a major accident hazard like a large chemical plant was involved. This machinery of mutual help has been adapted to changing needs, but in essence London still relies for its ultimate protection on a plan to combat what is now probably the least likely hazard that faces it.

The Thames tidal flood plan was not activated during the storm. There was no marked difference in need from borough to borough. Southern ones were worse-hit than northern ones, but only slightly so. A few boroughs made requests to their neighbours for equipment, but everyone was affected, and nobody had cranes, ladders or chainsaws to spare.

In the eyes of the emergency planners, the storm does not rate as much of a disaster at all. Even the King's Cross fire a few weeks later, in which 30 victims died, was handled within the emergency arrangements of Camden, the borough involved. The gale was no more than an "Operation Snowfall" emergency, where each department puts its own plan into effect, and calls up its own contacts.

"It worked perfectly, as much as anything can work in those sort of circumstances", says Max Tankard, emergency planning officer for Camden, whose borough emergency manual runs to about 50 pages.

Camden's tree surgeons were out on the streets as early as 2.30 am. The council employs three, but it was able in addition to call up several contractors who do regular work for it. The council's own direct labour force of plumbers, heating and ventilation engineers and so on were out on the streets soon after dawn. In all, Camden had some 80 workers out clearing up the damage. According to council staff who were perhaps rather carried away with the thrill of it all, some workers remained on the job for 48 hours without taking a break. The council – only one out of the 32 in London – handled 2,000 emergency calls in the first day alone.

Close contact was kept with police and electicity workers, and as news of trees leaning on houses or power lines came in, the town hall assessed the priorities for using the council's 30-ton crane and its fleet of vehicles equipped with mechanical shovels and three-ton cranes. There were about 500 trees down in the borough on the public highways alone, though not all of them were blocking the way. This reckoning excludes the 1,000 trees killed or injured on Hampstead Heath and the large number lying on private property, which it was the owners' responsibility to remove.

Meanwhile social services workers were going round evacuating people whose houses were dangerous or open to the rain. The torrential downpour which followed a few hours behind the gale sought out many lost tiles and fractured roof-edges which had gone unnoticed at first. Thousands of houses had suffered minor damage, and hundreds were more seriously affected. But the structural damage was not in general as severe as it had been in towns further south, and city services had such ample resources to call on that immediate problems were dealt with relatively quickly.

Hospitals these days are equipped with their own emergency generators to ensure that a general power cut cannot throw all their delicate operations into disarray. In spite of widespread damage to buildings, London's hospitals came through the night without serious difficulties, except for Charing Cross, where the failure of the back-up system cut off the power supply to one patient who was on a life support machine. Two nurses pumped the ventilator by hand for three hours to keep the patient alive.

It was a mortifying night for Independent Radio News. A storm emergency is one of the occasions when local radio should have a chance to come into its own. Loss of power blacks out television almost entirely. Ruined lines sever telephone links. Radio becomes the natural means of communication for many households at such moments, just when everyone is hungry for information. Radio messages to battery receivers could help to save listeners from real dangers, as well as bringing information and reassurance.

Out in the shires, some local radio stations were already in action performing their designated role in local emergency schemes. In London, the BBC was hit with a partial loss of power, and quickly made arrangements to squeeze extra public service information between programmes.

But Independent Radio News lost both power and telephones at 5.40 am, and was unable to re-establish communications for three hours. Without any messages coming in from its reporters, it had nothing but studio reports to transmit to its 47 network stations. Even the 8 am news bulletin had to be relayed by torchlight from the engineer's master control room with a single microphone, passed from hand to hand.

None of London's historic buildings came to any great harm. The great dome of St Paul's, 365 feet above ground level, must have endured wind forces comparable to the 96 mph gust recorded on the Post Office Tower. But it survived with the loss of a few window panes.

"This building is like a boulder in a stream", a verger told Brian James of *The Times* next morning. "Even in moderate winds it suffers. We have a safety staff who climb up on nights like that. Last night they had to cling together like men on a mountain to reach the roof".

Several of the plane trees round the cathedral came down, and in the morning its coigns and parapets were garlanded with broken boughs, with an effect inappropriately festive and faintly Mad-Hatterish. Where the chapter house of Old St Paul's had once stood, one tree fell and crushed the wrist of the modern statue of St Thomas a Becket, depicted toppling to the ground at the moment of his martyrdom.

It was in its trees that London suffered most, and of its trees, the plane was the chief casualty. There was a warning in this. The plane has for 200 years been the London tree *par excellence*. It has been asserted that it makes up no less than 60 per cent of the capital's stock of trees. Its fast growth, good looks and readiness to tolerate the air pollution which choked the city until the 1950s made it an automatic choice for parks and avenues. But 60 per cent is a dangerously high proportion, and the heavy losses the storm inflicted on London's planes were a reminder that it is bad forestry to put too many eggs in one basket. An epidemic like Dutch Elm Disease among planes would denude London of trees to an extent which would make the ravages of the storm look trivial.

The morning showed splendid plane trees lying in ruins on all sides, distinguished by that pale vellum bark which is exposed as outer layers, clogged with soot, are sloughed off like the skin of snakes. They lay along the Embankment, down The Mall and around London's green eighteenth- and nineteenth-century squares, Bedford Square, Russell Square, Bloomsbury Square and the rest. Several crushed the railings around the Tower of London, which had to be closed next day because of the danger – the first time it has ever had to close for a full day for safety reasons.

It was a plane that crushed Terence Marrin in Lincoln's Inn Fields. A few hundred yards away, another fell in Red Lion Square, and overthrew one of London's most endearing statues, that of Lord Brockway. It represented that durable Fabian and pacifist as if addressing a Conway Hall rally on behalf of some overlooked Commonwealth minority, and gesturing towards the moral high ground in a billowing 1950s suit. This accident conferred on Lord Brockway, then a few weeks short of his hundredth year, a distinction almost certainly unique in modern times. It is rare for a statue to be raised in anybody's honour in a London street in his lifetime. Brockway must have been alone today in having seen his statue raised, and also felled by what more superstitious generations would have called an Act of God. He bore the omen with fortitude, however.

The fall of trees produced another effect of fortuitous symbolism on Islington Green, where the morning showed a pathetic group of casualties brushing with their leaves the foot of a stone cenotaph erected as a war memorial. Its inscription, "In Memory of the Fallen" had acquired a double meaning in the night.

The Royal Parks were transformed by the storm into a jungle: pathways where the cream of society had been wheeled in their prams by generations of nannies were lost under masses of withering foliage, and any gust of air could bring down a tree or a bough which had been mortally wounded but remained pinned aloft by its neighbours. The overnight losses in the Royal Parks were more than 3,000, and another 2,000 were so badly damaged that there would be little alternative to felling them too. Nearly 600 were down in Hyde Park and Kensington Gardens alone, where hastily-daubed placards were hung on the locked gates to keep out spectators disposed to risk their necks.

From Green Park, where the trees are rooted in the soil of a long-abandoned cemetery, to Greenwich where they were planted as raw material for future battleships, London's parkland was left in ruins. St James's Park, Richmond, Hampton Court, Regent's Park, Kenwood and Ham Common all suffered. But the most shocking and irreparable damage was done at Kew Gardens and in the Chelsea Physic Garden. Both are botanical collections more than 200 years old, and the former is the definitive collection of its kind in this country. It would take days even to compute the losses.

Many of the trees lost at Syon Park in west London were veterans of yet another ravaged eighteenth-century landscaping scheme. But one of them brought about in its fall a more unusual loss: it toppled onto the London Butterfly House, a greenhouse-like structure which has been built in the park and kept at tropical temperatures for a living display of exotic butterflies which hang from sultry palm-leaves or sip sugar laid out for their pleasure. Gigantic hirsute spiders brood in the humid undergrowth as well.

The structural damage was estimated at £3,000. The broken glass allowed 300 butterflies to escape – blue *Morphopeleides* from Trinidad, Brazilian Owls, Blue Mormons from Sri Lanka, and Autumn Leaves from Malaysia, some up to seven inches in wing-span.

Of all the strange legends of the storm, perhaps the most bizarre was that of a cloud of iridescent blue tropical butterflies being whisked helplessly across the Home Counties by a tempest of tropical provenance and ferocity. Similar incidents happened to butterfly centres at Enfield, Weymouth and Great Yarmouth – where more than 1,000 butterflies of 85 different species were lost from the seafront centre. It is tempting to imagine the storm belt as having been alive with tropical butterflies from one end to another; though sadly there is no record of any late traveller battling through the surrealistic frenzy of the gale, and finding gaudy insects fluttering around his head.

In fact, most of the lost butterflies probably escaped not in the night, when they would have been quiescent, but in the early morning, when the bright sun woke them up. At Syon, the staff were out with butterfly nets trying to catch the insects as they danced through the broken panes. The wind was still strong, and many of the escaping butterflies must have been torn to pieces on wires and branches within a few minutes.

On his wild drive into London along the Cromwell Road, Douglas Nye paused at a red light outside the Natural History Museum, pulling over as far into the right-hand lane as possible, in case one of the noble row of plane trees at the front of the museum might choose that moment to topple down on him. A taxi driver with a strange taste for adversity drew up alongside him, and they exchanged grimaces. The wind rocked both cars on their springs as they waited for the lights to change. Then Nye was off again on the way to *The Observer*'s office at St Andrew's Hill.

Not one of that row of planes fell in the night, as it happened, though they scattered many branches onto the road. One tree which stands among them, and emerged unscathed as well, was the oldest tree of all the millions in Britain buffeted by the storm that night. Gnarled and cracked, its fissures now caulked with cement, it is a cinnamon-coloured torso about 20 feet high, which has not put out a green shoot since long before there was such a thing as a plane tree on earth.

It dates from the Lower Carboniferous age, 350 million years ago, and its fossilised remains were excavated in Scotland in the middle of the last century. It has been standing beside the museum about as long as the trees around it, but it is roughly three million times as old as they are. It flourished long before the time of the earliest dinosaurs, when Scotland was covered by a humid tropical jungle, devoid of butterflies but with dragonflies two feet wide whirring through its glades. What storms this tree may have bowed to in its lifetime we cannot guess: but it is quite possible that it never met the equal of that of last October.

CHAPTER 14

ONE HOME IN SIX

*"It was dangerous to walk the streets, the bricks and tiles
falling from the houses, that the whole streets were covered
with them and whole chimneys, nay, whole houses in two or
three places, blowed down."*
(Samuel Pepys, *Diary*, London, January 24, 1666:
"The Great Storme")

Among other things, a house is a machine for sheltering us from the wind.
On the night of the great storm, thousands of houses obviously fell short in
that elementary function. Architects will be mulling over the lessons of
October 16, 1987, for years to come.

The direct structural damage was only the beginning of the story. The
torn and abraded roofs left many homes open to the torrential rain which
followed a few hours after. The Association of British Insurers estimate that
one household in six in southern England covered by insurance suffered
damage as a result of the storm. The total cost of structural damage, insured
and uninsured, was in the neighbourhood of a billion pounds – and three-
quarters of this involved domestic property.

Scores of people were injured by structural failures, and at least four
were killed. For many others, like the Thomas family in the Robert de
Mortain public house, it was only chance that saved their lives, not any protective virtues in their dwellings.

But the reaction of the architectural profession, including the Royal
Institute of British Architects, has been that the storm not only failed to
expose any flaws in today's building regulations, but actually vindicated
them by a test far beyond any everyday trials.

That verdict would have rung hollowly in the ears of the householders of
Peacehaven, as they settled down to face weeks of life in whatever corner of
their shattered homes could still be made waterproof, or arranged to have
their rain-damaged furnishings put into store before moving in on friends
or relations until their homes could be repaired.

A host of satisfied opportunists might have ridiculed the official view in
a more cheerful spirit. Any cowboy with a tarpaulin, or an Acrow jack for
propping up swaying walls, was able to name his own price for renting it
out, for weeks afterwards.

Some architects, at least, still have fears that the stresses inflicted on
large buildings that night may have done them inner harm which may not
become apparent until much later.

But on a broad view, there is obviously a good deal in the official verdict. Practically everyone was under a roof that night, yet practically everyone survived. The list of casualties shows that statistically a house was an exceedingly safe place to be in. A car was much more dangerous. Most people who looked out at the open air decided rightly that they were safer under cover. Trees made a nasty mess of many houses, yet only one death was caused in this way.

Even where flat roofs flew away, they generally did so without harming a hair of the head of the people cowering beneath them. Only one of the innumerable flat roofs in flight over the home counties landed on top of someone when it came down again.

On one page of Britain's official code of standards for building design appears a map of the country which looks at first sight like a weather forecaster's chart. In a sense that is what it is. It is a map of the maximum wind speeds which designers should allow for in different parts of the country. In the north and on high ground it is necessary to build to higher standards than in the south-east.

Taking account of past records, the map was intended to show Britain under the windiest conditions that it seemed prudent to take precautions against. Mean wind speeds had never even touched these hypothetical extremes in the ten years since the code was imposed. Yet on October 15–16, the extremes were exceeded almost everywhere in the storm belt.

It is in this context that the profession greeted the performance of the country's buildings with a sigh of relief. The exceptional character of the storm is pointed up in cold figures by a survey of building failures made in 1986 by the Building Research Establishment (the BRE). It found that on average 200,000 buildings a year are damaged in gales, at an average annual cost of £35,500,000 – of which the greater part reflects the cost of a small number of major failures in industrial buildings.

In the 1987 storm, industrial building suffered no less than £200 million-worth of damage. Yet this was no more than a third as much as the overall loss suffered by individual families in at least a million homes. No other weather catastrophe in the last ten years –probably none since 1947 – cost even half as much in real terms, nor fell so heavily on families.

The storm was extraordinary in the scale of its damage, but the kind of harm it did was less unusual. The BRE's study analysed the 181 deaths and serious injuries caused by building failures in gales in the United Kingdom between 1962 and 1984. It recorded 26 deaths and 23 serious injuries due to chimney falls. Roof failures led to 14 deaths and 30 serious injuries, and collapsing walls claimed a similar number of deaths and injuries.

Between them, these three causes – chimneys, roofs and walls – accounted for 60 per cent of the 86 fatal casualties in that 22-year period. Bursting windows – something which people were understandably worried about in 1987 – had killed only two. Scaffoldings, hoardings and signs had killed two more. Tree damage to a house had caused one death and no serious injuries. Lamp standards caused not one death or serious injury. Caravans killed five. The average annual total of deaths was five.

In other words, the gale of October 16, passing over one corner of Britain, accounted in four hours for the equivalent of a normal year's toll of deaths and injuries from gale damage to buildings over the whole country. The figures suggest that if it had arrived when people were up and about, the number of casualties would have been greater, with collapsing walls and roofs hurting many more people. Setting the force of the storm side by side with the casualty list, we got off lightly.

The great killer in 1987, true to precedent, was the chimney stack. Four of the five deaths caused by building failures were caused by chimneys, and many of the closest narrow escapes.

The record would probably have been worse a few years ago. Stricter regulations were introduced in the 1970s to ensure that flat roofs were built with more effective fastenings to the walls, after a number of cases of gale damage. Many roofs damaged in October dated from before that change, so the architectural establishment could claim that present-day rules had not been found wanting.

The fear that made structural engineers sleep uneasily that night was the possibility that some major modern building would suffer a progressive collapse. Conventional structures, like most homes, are built very much in line with the traditional rules of thumb developed over many decades. Large industrial buildings and high blocks of flats are built with much greater dependence on theory, and are designed closer to the theoretical limits of safety, because the cost savings involved can be substantial. When the breeze makes the windows rattle, structural engineers wonder if there is anything they missed in their calculations, and remember Ronan Point.

Ronan Point was the block of flats in East London where a small gas explosion in 1968 blew out a wall panel which started a progressive collapse as it fell, killing five people and showing the whole building to be a potential deathtrap. It was eventually demolished, but it still symbolises the dangers of any design that ventures into untried fields of technology.

"These tall buildings rise to heights where our records of wind speeds at ground level are no guide to what happens", says Sam Webb, an architect who was involved in the investigations after the disaster. "When the Met Office say that a wind like October's comes once every 300 years, I take that with a pinch of salt. While we were demolishing Ronan Point, we had winds of 90 mph at the top when there was virtually no wind below."

Like the Eddystone Lighthouse, tower blocks are designed to yield a little to the wind. At the height of the storm, some tenants of the Barbican flats in the City came down to sit in the foyer because the 400-foot towers, the tallest residential buildings in Europe, were perceptibly swaying. They are concrete frame structures of immense strength, but still they move. Regulations allow a block to sway a foot for every 180 feet of its height.

Many tall 1960s buildings still exist with structural similarities to Ronan Point. Dougal Gonsal in Camden and Ian Gordon, Assistant Director of

Housing (Technical) in Greenwich, both had anxieties that night about tall buildings in their care, especially ones faced with panels of concrete or brickwork, which suction forces might tear out. Hawkridge, the block in Camden which was evacuated three years ago, because of fears for its safety, came through unscathed. One 16-storey block in Battersea had sections sucked out, and a ten-storey block in Greenwich lost a panel. The possibility that other panels might have been weakened could only be checked by means of expensive tests.

But high technology came through the night relatively well in general. It was among smaller, older properties that the most widespread damage was done, in Camden, in Greenwich and throughout the south-east. Those tumbling chimneys were mainly on older buildings, and they carried more lessons about maintenance than design.

"It wasn't old buildings as such that failed to stand up to the gale", says Mr Gordon. "We did have a lot of trouble with purpose-built cottage estates about 60 years old, coming to the end of their design lives and needing renovation. But we also have a good deal of older stock – Victorian terraces which often came into our hands in poor condition and have already been renovated. They stood up very well. One post-war estate was waiting for a £1,250,000 roofing job, which had been delayed by spending cuts. Every second house there had roof damage."

The wider story was similar. Older buildings in good condition would shed tiles and sometimes a few bits of masonry, but their integrity was usually untouched. The storm which devastated so many historic parks did remarkably little damage to historic buildings. Elizabethan mansions with exuberant outgrowths of ornamental chimneys, tithe barns and water mills with timber frames 500 years old, castles standing on foundations laid by the Romans and cathedrals with 300-foot spires – almost all survived that dark night with only superficial harm.

There were some failures, but not many. A finial broke off from one of the outrageous pinnacles of the Brighton Pavilion and crashed through the floor of the Music Room, to perch like an unexploded shell half-submerged in the brand new carpet. But it was only dislodged because of movements in the scaffolding put up for renovations. Chichester Cathedral suffered some minor damage. St Osyth's Priory in Essex lost a whole platoon of chimney stacks. At Waxham in Norfolk, an important medieval barn partially collapsed; historic farm buildings are a relatively disregarded and poorly documented category, and suffered especially heavy losses, which farmers may often lack the resources to repair. But on the whole, the custodians of historic buildings were able to share the architects' relief.

The fact that ancient buildings came through so well indicates that they were in reasonably good condition. Credit for this is due to their owners, public or private, and also says something for the assistance available for those seeking to renovate decrepit gems of architecture. It also says a great deal for the skills of the builders of the past.

"You could say that if such buildings have lasted several hundred years, they must have the qualities needed to ride out storms like that'', says Robert Chitham, director of the historic buildings division of English Heritage. "It is probably true that generally they are in better repair than a couple of generations ago. But the reason they stay up is in a sense the opposite of the reason modern buildings do.

"Today's buildings are designed on very precise and generous parameters in terms of strength of materials. With older ones, a lot of rule of thumb was involved. The buildings were designed on very flexible principles, so that they get away with things even if they have weak points through poor maintenance and so on.

"During the war it was found that timber frame buildings were pretty well indestructible from blast. Some survived bombing even though the infill between the frames had been almost totally blown away."

Charles Winder's 300-year-old house, mentioned in chapter nine, is a case in point.

In Defoe's storm of 1703, the damage seems to have been far more extensive than it was in 1987. But this is probably less a sign of fundamental defects than a reflection of the conditions of a period without building regulations, mortgages or improvement grants. Many houses of the time would probably have seemed to us half-ruinous even without a storm.

Until the middle of the nineteenth century, buildings of all kinds were built with lime mortar. This is more flexible than modern mortar, based on Portland cement, but less adhesive. It helps to make older buildings more yielding, more liable to subsidiary failure, but less liable to catastrophic collapse. The weak adhesion of lime mortar helped to topple many older chimneys, which sheared off easily.

Modern science could no doubt devise a roof tile which it would be impossible for any imaginable wind to dislodge. But it would cost too much to be worth fitting. It a tile blows off, it can be replaced without much trouble. Old tiled roofs and modern ones both have their weaknesses, but they are of opposite kinds. In the past, when labour was cheap and steel expensive, tiles were pinned to the roof-battens with timber pegs, and smeared on the underside with an evil-smelling preparation, made of straw mixed with clay or dung, which was called 'torching', and provided a measure of insulation while effectively glueing the tiles in place.

The torching has often crumbled away over the centuries, and the wooden pegs may have deteriorated too, leaving the tiles virtually lying in their places waiting to be whisked away.

These days we have high labour costs, cheap steel and roofing-felt. Tiles are laid on the battens quickly, with metal pins. But to save labour, these are often put in only on every third row, with the pinned rows holding the other rows in place. The felt underneath does not give the same adhesion as torching used to. Once a pinned row of tiles starts to break away, the unpinned rows beside them have nothing to hold them down, and wide areas of roofing can fly off on the wind.

No wonder so many tiles went astray on October 15–16. But most of them were replaced within a matter of days. In the normal way, they could be counted as a sustainable loss. It is only in the rare storms of extreme intensity that failure of the tiles – especially where there is no inner layer to stop the wind streaming into the roof cavity – gives a severe storm the purchase it needed to wrest away gable ends and dislodge whole roofs.

All architecture must involve a trade-off between strength and cost or effort. The craftsman builders of the past and the engineer builders of today have used different compromises in the solutions they have to find to this permanent problem. It is a natural instinct, and a proper one, to ask who is to blame after any major catastrophe – and a catastrophe which cost about £1 billion in bricks and mortar is a major one by any standards.

But it would be wrong to make scapegoats of the architects for failing to make full provision for an eventuality which arises once every 300 years. Spread out over that period, even £1 billion appears as a relatively manageable sum. It is certainly far less than what it would cost to make buildings so strong that they could stand up to the worst storm that can possibly be imagined. Long before most of them ever met that test, the time would come when they would reach the end of their natural lives, and the extra strength would just make it more difficult to demolish them.

It would be as unfair to blame architects for failing to prevent the destruction which occurred during that unique night as it would be to blame them for not having installed fireproofing in our homes up to the standard which will be needed to protect us all on the day of the Last Judgment.

CHAPTER 15

HIGH TIDE

"People can't die, along the coast", said Mr Peggotty, "except when the tide's pretty nigh out. They can't be born, unless its pretty nigh in – not properly born till flood . . . If he lives till it turns, he'll hold his own till past the flood, and go out with the next tide."

(Charles Dickens: *David Copperfield*)

Douglas Nye slid his typescript through *The Observer*'s letter box on St Andrew's Hill. It was 3 am. A dustbin clattered past, with a little tornado of papers pouring upwards out of it, and a crash of broken glass came from somewhere nearby. He ducked back into his car and dodged his way along the Embankment, sometimes on the road, sometimes on the pavement. He drove out of London past Kew to Twickenham.

"The dual carriageway there had become just a quivering, twitching, shaggy green carpet of twigs and leaves. Larger boughs, fallen trees, humped into view merely as islands in the green, projecting tentacles flailing in the gale. We had to weave lock-to-lock, dodging the major obstacles. Incredible – airborne boughs the size of decent Christmas trees hurtled bodily, left to right, across the road ahead.

"A car in front took a bough on its left-front – its driver OK but stopping. It was like a torpedoed ship reeling away from a wartime convoy, leaving its consorts to struggle on. I'm going home."

The wind had been behind him on the run to London, but now its full force confronted the car, which he kept moving at 40–55 mph. At the Sunbury flyover, he drove "up onto that familiar elevated left-hand curve. Suddenly, in a terrific gust, the steering wheel went slack; my arms almost crossed, I thought the steering had broken . . . then rubber squealed, the Savanna swerved. I corrected. It drove on normally. Presumably its front wheels had been lifted from the road."

He had hoped that by the time he attempted the return journey the wind would have blown itself out. But it was as strong as ever, and much more debris had piled up by now, even on the motorway. In the narrow, tree-lined roads after the motorway, it was far worse. "Round one fallen tree's topmost branches through a fortuitously-sited lay-by, round another behind the pumps in an equally fortuitous filling-station forecourt. Round another up the kerb and along the verge. I'm going home."

At about 4.10 am, he made it, to find the drive blocked by three of his own small cypresses, which he had to heave aside before he could rejoin his wide-awake family, who must have been wondering whether he would ever reappear.

Not everyone on the roads was as lucky. The Doke family in South London were just getting out of bed by then, ready to drive to Gatwick for their holiday flight to Spain. The airport had in fact been closed, and their flight postponed. They tried to telephone in case the gale had affected flight schedules, but the lines were down and they could not get through. Rather than risk missing their plane, they set out with their luggage, driven by John Doke's brother Robert.

There were five of them in the car: Robert Doke at the wheel, with John and Hazel Doke and their 11-year-old daughter Kerry, and their 13-year-old son Lee, who was sitting behind his uncle.

"We were laughing about the wind, we didn't realise how serious it was", says Mrs Hazel Doke. "We saw trees lying on the road and drove round them. All the street lamps had gone off because of the power cut, of course. We had to try several routes. Either we found we couldn't get through, or we met cars coming the other way, who told us the way was blocked. There was quite a lot of traffic – it was getting on for six by then."

Eventually they reached Croydon, about eight miles from their Catford home, and got onto the main road.

"John's brother was never one to give up – we asked him to go back several times, but he was determined to find a way through. We never thought we were in danger. We came to a fallen tree, and Robert was just slowing down to go round it when suddenly another tree came down on the car.

"It happened so suddenly in the dark. We never saw or heard any warning before it hit us.

"Robert was killed outright. The driver's side of the car was completely crushed, and Lee was trapped inside. We scrambled out. We couldn't believe the way the car had just been smashed. It was like a nightmare: 'Is this really happening, or am I going to wake up in a minute?'

"We couldn't get Lee out. It was dreadful. Luckily there was a Post Office sorting office just near, and they all came out to help. Someone had a car with a crane, and with the help of that they were able to cut Lee out. The local people were wonderful."

By the time the police had managed to reach the scene, the car was empty and the family on their way to hospital. John and Lee were given head x-rays, and John was kept in hospital for observation, but none of them were seriously hurt.

Robert Doke was married, with two teenage daughters. He might have been only one of a much larger number of fatalities on the roads if the wind had not begun to drop just at the time that early morning travellers were beginning to set out. Mrs Doke noticed that cars were already coming out in significant numbers, although by 6 am the BBC was issuing warnings to travellers, and the streets were a veritable Palm Sunday of strewn boughs. Many were venturing out to battle their way to work, regardless of danger.

At 6 am the gale's impetus was on the point of weakening. Yet it could still summon up gusts as destructive as ever. In fact, it is notable that some of the most tragic accidents caused by land and sea happened in these last hours – and some of the most notable feats of courage.

It appears that the hours of pounding may have had a cumulative effect on structures, weakening them to a point where they finally had to yield. If that is the case, one may speculate that just another hour or half-hour of peak winds might have left behind a disproportionate havoc. The damage to trees must certainly have had a cumulative character, as the night went on and the working of the roots in the ground gradually loosened their grip.

It was 6.15 am when a chimney fell in Hove and crushed Mrs Beryl Agha to death in her sleep. Tons of masonry and rubble poured into her bedroom. Seconds later, the bedroom floor gave way and the rubble, the bed and Mrs Agha fell ten feet into the room downstairs. She must have been killed instantly. Her teenage daughters Melissa and Michele, asleep on the same floor, escaped unhurt. It took council workers seven hours before they were able to recover the body.

The beech tree 40 miles to the north which smashed the roof of the Bardells' home in Wrotham, as described in chapter nine, must have fallen at almost the same moment – luckily without causing serious injury.

It was 6.25 am when a chimney of the Harte and Garter Hotel in Windsor, 40 miles west of Wrotham, fell and killed Mrs Patricia Bellwood. She was a social services consultant from Newcastle-upon-Tyne, and was staying in the hotel while lecturing in Reading on child abuse. Firemen burrowed through rubble and broken beams, in danger of a further collapse, and found Mrs Bellwood buried up to her waist and already dead. The two floors below had to be supported with hydraulic jacks before her body could be removed safely.

Robert Homewood, aged 59, of Beacon Hill Farm, Biddenden, Kent, was in bed when two chimney stacks and half the roof caved in and wiped out his room. "He had just been to see our mother to tell her not to be worried by the storm", said his brother Alec. "He didn't stand a chance".

Mrs Sosammi Shilling was crushed to death in her bed in Chatham by a falling 60-foot beech tree. Police dug through the debris with bare hands to release her, but it was too late. She was the only person in the storm to be killed outright by a falling tree while indoors. But 67-year-old Miss Georgina Wells was so badly injured by a tree which fell onto her home in Penn Crescent, Haywards Heath, that she died five days later in hospital.

All the other fatalities caused by trees were either on the roads or outdoors, or afterwards among those helping in the dangerous task of clearing up the damage.

The late rush of accidents was attributed to another factor by some witnesses whose trade was connected with the sea. The wind dropped, they said, as high tide passed and the tide began to ebb. The suggestion was put forward only in a half-superstitious spirit. It must have been the case, at least, that many vessels otherwise sheltered by features on land would have been most exposed at high water. Whatever the reason was, the biggest maritime stories did begin just about now.

At 5 am the 935-ton cargo ship *Union Mars*, registered in Dublin, put out a distress call from a position three miles south of St Catherine's Point, the rocky southernmost headland of the Isle of Wight. On passage from Fowey in Cornwall to Rotterdam, she had been forced to turn round to face the wind, hoping to mark time till it moderated. But an enormous wave, 40 feet high, smashed much of the wheelhouse and tore off a door. With most of his navigation equipment gone and his lights out of action, the skipper could no longer steer against the tempest from the south, which was blowing his ship towards the cliffs.

Yarmouth and Bembridge lifeboats were alerted. The Yarmouth lifeboat normally takes six to eight minutes to get under way in an emergency: but this time it was over an hour before they could move, because crewmen could not reach the town along roads blocked by trees. Brian Miskin, the mechanic, gave up trying to drive and ran the four miles from his home.

The usual course for the Yarmouth lifeboat on making for the open sea would be to turn left at the harbour entrance, and use the North Channel past the Needles rocks. But the gale was so strong that even a lifeboat had to think twice about confronting it, against the last of the rising tide. The boat turned right on leaving harbour, and sailed with the tide at full speed right along the Solent, meaning to join the Bembridge boat and come into the open at the other end of the island.

"I have never seen anything like it", Mr D.Kennedy, coxwain of the Yarmouth boat, told the local paper afterwards, in a refrain that was repeated a thousand times all across the storm country. "Had the coaster sent a full 'Mayday', indicating that she was about to sink, we would have gone out through the North Channel. But that wasn't the situation.

"Even in the Solent the waves were 15 feet high, and round the back of the island the further out you got the worse the conditions were. We had reports of 70-foot waves in the Channel Islands area."

The conditions were so bad that it was thought necessary to have two lifeboats to tackle the job, and mobile shore units had been alerted at Bembridge and Ventnor. The latter did not get far: just as they were leaving the town, large trees came down ahead of them and behind, and their share in the rescue was at an end.

This particular joke was one that the storm had been playing with undiminished gusto for hours. An ambulance making a call in Bembridge to take an elderly woman to hospital was pinned down in just the same way by trees ahead and astern. It had to be rescued by firemen before it could start its five-mile run to Ryde – a trip which took it an hour and a half, even with its escort of firemen.

But by the time the Yarmouth lifeboat had reached Bembridge, the wind was veering more to the west, as it had done some four hours before in the Channel Islands. The crippled ship was carried clear of St Catherine's, and was able eventually to get into Portsmouth under her own power.

The *Union Mars* limped past within view of another shipwreck, of a kind – the wreck of a construction which had spent almost a century at sea, though not afloat. Shanklin Pier was a 93-year-old survivor of the days of brass-binnacled paddle steamers and beer-and-pork-pie excursions by whiskery Edwardians resolute on having a good time. But it had been leading a precarious existence for many stormy years. Salt air was rusting its ironwork, its theatre and amusement arcade had grown shabby, and holidaymakers had grown used to looking elsewhere for their pleasures.

But it had been bought for a song by a Southampton leisure company the year before, and they had sought planning permission only a few days before the storm for a £4.5 million development plan, to include a disco, fast food area, multi-storey car park and bathing flume.

Before a decision could be taken, the storm carried away the whole middle section of the pier, including the theatre and amusement arcade. More than half its length disappeared under the waves. Tons of debris were scattered far along the beach, and more drifted away on the tide. The pier had been battered to pieces at the very moment when a new role seemed to be opening up for it.

More than 70 miles to the east, the fishermen on Hastings beach were engaged in an all-night struggle to secure their boats. They keep their chunky 30-foot luggers on the open shingle, and launch them at all seasons to catch sole, cod or plaice.

"We had to keep moving the boats higher because the sea kept coming forward", says Paul Joy, secretary of the Hastings Fishermen's Protection Society. "It was above the usual high-tide level two hours before high water, although it should have been nearly the smallest tide of the year. You have to check on the boats all the time if the wind 'goes open' – if it comes in from the sea.

"Everyone had stopped fishing hours before – no boat could put to sea in such weather. My 80-year-old father was down there helping, and he said he had never experienced anything like it. One 11-ton boat was picked up and thrown into the lifeboat shed.

"There are winches at the top of the beach to pull the boats up, and a crew member always stays ashore to look after the winch. He is called the 'boy ashore'. It is a job for the older men. Each one looks after about three boats, and takes his wages as a percentage of the takings of the boats.

"It was so dark you couldn't see much of what was happening. About 3 am, a concrete winch-shed blew down on top of the chap inside, called Richard Adams. He got cut about quite badly. Two of us took him up to hospital, leaving just one man there, Mr Read."

James Read, an experienced fisherman of 49 who had been working at Hastings for 12 years, had just finished heaving one winch up and was walking to another when they last saw him. When they got back from the hospital, he seemed to have left the beach. They went to the Angling Club, a tea-shop which opens early for the sake of the fishermen.

"I was just coming out of the Angling Club when I heard someone say 'There's someone under there'. It was just getting light by then. The wooden roof of the shed was in a different spot, and there was a man lying under it.

"Four of us lifted the roof off, and cleaned his face to see who it was. It was Mr Read. He must have been walking past the shed towards the club when a gust lifted the roof up and over and on top of him. He was blue and his tongue was sticking out, but he was moving. We thought he was alive. We commandeered a truck and drove it up to the hospital, all over the fallen trees. But the doctors there said that he was clinically dead, with some functions still working. It was a one in a million chance that he was walking past, and alone, just as the roof flipped over."

Eastward again, the cross-Channel ferry *Hengist* was safely tied up in port at Folkestone. At least, Jim Ewing, the port manager, had thought that the 5,590-ton ship would be safe when he heard the evening forecast.

"If we'd had the right information, our dear old *Hengist* wouldn't have landed on the rocks, because he woudn't have stayed in port", he says. He calls the *Hengist* 'he' and 'she' indifferently, but I did not hear him call her 'it'. There were 22 crew on board the ship – cleaners, caterers and so on as well as seamen – but no passengers.

"He was secured for storm conditions at 24 points, with warps ranging from six inches circumference to twelve-inch, and one or two 3½-inch wires as well. These new polypropylene multiplant ropes are very strong, with more give than wire.

"As regards the conditions we experienced, they were nothing like the forecast. Folkestone is an exposed harbour in certain directions. The ship should have been safe in a south-westerly wind, but it was south-south west. If we had known it was going to be, the ship might have set off to ride out the storm at sea. We had extra staff on duty on the shore, because of the weather: the junior manager and eight of my staff, instead of only four. Each mooring line was replaced as it went. A continuous wall of water was sweeping over the pier, and £140,000 worth of damage was done.

"When the ship started parting moorings, she was on standby. The master had got her engines started, and he went to sea. But the ship was rolling so much that the engines tripped out. The propellors were lifting out of the water, and there is a governor, designed to cut in automatically and stop them when they lift, so they don't damage themselves.

"The lights had gone out on the shore by now, but the ship's lights were working. Then they went out as she moved away and the wind caught her. The people on shore thought she was going to roll right over. But her lights went on again, and she drifted down onto the Warren. She grounded at about 5.30, about an hour before high water.

"We had it at the back of our minds that the ship might break up. It was a shingle beach, but she ended up against one corner of a concrete groyne, which actually holed her. But at first the wind was so strong that there was no attempt to get the crew off.

"High water was at 6.30, and after that there was a definite lull – you could cut it with a knife, so you could define the exact moment of high tide. I was at home, and I'd been in touch by phone since 3 am. I said to myself: If my windows are going in – for it sounded as if they might – they'll go before 6.30. After that I knew they were safe".

Coastguards, police and firemen were drawn up on the beach waiting for their chance, and as soon as the wind moderated all but a skeleton crew were brought ashore with a breeches buoy along a cable. There was still a huge sea running, sending jets of spray up the ship's side. The edge of the concrete platform on the beach had punched a hole ten feet by eight feet in the hull close to the waterline.

Folkestone's busier neighbour, Dover, is a much better sheltered harbour with wide-embracing sea walls like those of Cherbourg. It has two entrances and is normally accessible in all weathers. Its 600-acre outer harbour is so large that it could have accommodated every ship in George V's Royal Navy at the height of the *Dreadnought* age.

The sea just north of Dover, called the Downs, has been for centuries a great refuge and a great graveyard of shipping. Defoe's famous storm of 1703 scattered a fleet of warships anchored in the Downs. Defoe asserts that the seamen of Deal, who normally traded with small open boats as miscellaneous ancillaries to ships waiting for a fair wind, put out eagerly in search of booty as the storm rose, and ignored the drowning sailors of the fleet.

With his characteristic eye for the graphic detail, Defoe reports that some victims managed to make their way onto the Goodwin Sands (which are exposed at low tide). But they were left to wait shivering for the rising tide to sweep them away, while the Deal 'hovellers' bustled through the waves rounding up casks of interesting merchandise.

However, some of the Deal men succeeded at great risk in rescuing 200 men. They were looked after in the town and sent to London at the Mayor's expense – for which the Admiralty never sent a penny of recompense. Altogether the week-long gale caused the loss of 15 of Queen Anne's ships, and 1,500 officers and men went down with them.

The morning after the gale of 1987, the media reported that Dover had been closed – for the first time in living memory, or the first time in 200 years, depending which paper you read. Harbour workers at Dover stoutly deny that it ever did close. They insist that it would have been contrary to all the traditions of the sea to have turned any vessel away if it had sought refuge there, and in practice impossible.

The controversy is an academic one. "It is one of these political things", says Jim Ewing. "We could say Folkestone wasn't closed, but it would have been foolhardy to enter. The last thing a master at sea in those conditions wants to do is to go into port and get smashed up. The only thing to do is to turn head to wind and sea and ride it out, with the engines just keeping you moving fast enough to steer".

Ferries which had set out to cross the Channel the night before were forced to adopt this policy. The Sealink vessels *St Christopher* and *St Nicholas* lay all night off Dover and Harwich with 800 passengers on board, waiting for the winds to moderate. The 8,000-ton *St Christopher*, which had left Calais on what is normally a 90-minute run at 3.30 am, rode out the storm in company with several other ferries and did not dock until 2 the following afternoon. A harbour spokesman conceded that this was "a thing we have not seen for many years".

Forty-foot waves had buckled the steel doors of the *St Christopher*'s upper car deck, allowing water to pour in. The ship was rolling so much that three lorries toppled over and slithered to and fro, crushing cars and damaging merchandise. Some passengers claimed as they came ashore from their ordeal that the crew had been ordered to chain up the lorries, and had refused to do so because of the danger; but Sealink denied this.

Meanwhile a great deal was going on in Dover itself. Minor incidents of damage to ships and harbour buildings began as early as 9 pm.

At 6.45 am, just at high tide, a ship tried to enter the harbour. She was the small coaster *Sumnia*, of 1,595 gross tons, which had been sheltering in the lee of Dungeness, and had dragged her anchors. She decided to make a run for it into Dover, after sending a 'Mayday' call at 5 am. She had been making a passage empty from London to Shoreham, to pick up a cargo of wheat. She carried a crew of six.

In certain gale conditions, a tide-race builds up off the south breakwater of Dover harbour. The *Sumnia* would have had to manoeuvre with wind and seas behind her and then turn broadside-on to them to get into the southern entrance of the harbour. A port tug went out to offer help, but apparently the *Sumnia* tried to turn the corner on her own. She was blown into the breakwater and suddenly tipped over.

The lifeboat was launched, commanded by acting coxwain Roy Couzens, a local garage owner in everyday life. "The seas were murderous. We could hardly see anything with huge waves, a wall of spray and lashing wind", said a coastguard. The lifeboat succeeded in snatching two men off the coaster's bow, and the tug rescued another, before a wave which one lifeboatman swore was 70 feet high engulfed the wrecked ship.

After a fruitless search for more survivors, the lifeboat turned for home. The sea was so violent near the south breakwater that Mr Couzens did not attempt the entrance the *Sumnia* had tried, but made a detour half a mile northward to the other entrance. It was only because of this that they caught sight of a hand in the water grasping a lifejacket, and rescued a fourth crew member, 21-year-old Mike Traynor, who was on the point of being swept past the harbour and away out to sea. He had swallowed a lot of oil and seemed to be dead when he was pulled into the lifeboat, but he recovered in hospital.

As the survivors were brought ashore and the lifeboat prepared to go out again to look for the two lost mariners, Roy Couzens, who had been thrown heavily against the wheel, realised that the chest pains he was feeling meant something worse than bruising. He was taken to Buckland Hospital – which like many other hospitals that night was operating on emergency power in the power cut – along with the men he had rescued, and was found to be suffering from a serious heart attack.

No trace was found of the missing men that night. The body of the *Sumnia*'s first mate, Ron Horlock, was eventually discovered a day later, flung by the waves onto the top of the breakwater. The master, David Birch of Belfast, was swept away altogether, and his body was never recovered.

It would take several chapters to recount all the emergencies by sea that night. The elderly 15,000-ton Polish cruise liner *Stefan Batory*, anchored in the Thames estuary, was heeled 15 degrees by the wind, and dragged and lost two anchors. At Felixstowe, the 1,300-ton tanker *Silverfalcon* went adrift and caused extensive damage. The ship was laden with propanol and other highly toxic and inflammable chemicals, and the port was closed for most of the day, and many families were evacuated from homes in the area, until the *Silverfalcon*, holed in several places and dripping with fire-resistant foam, was towed away and secured in Ipswich.

Further north, rescue services kept watch on another unfolding story, which might have turned into by far the most serious of all the night's disasters. A 10,000-ton semi-submersible pipe-laying rig blessed with the name *Smit Semi One* broke from its anchors 40 miles off Cromer, grazed a sandbank which put its bow engine and steering out of action, and drifted north towards two drilling rigs. Standing fixed on the sea bed, they were unable to get out of its way. Tugs followed the vagrant for hours, and helicopters flew overhead trying to drop a tow-line aboard. Eventually, a Dutch supply vessel called *Smit Lloyd 26* took the drifting ship under tow.

Meanwhile, 40 men had been evacuated from one of the rigs, the *Bonanza Zapata*, by helicopter – a stressful operation in those conditions. But the 79 men aboard the pipe-layer included four divers in a decompression chamber. After a deep underwater dive, it is necessary to acclimatise back to atmospheric pressure gradually. The nitrogen in the bloodstream is apt to effervesce if pressure falls too rapidly for the blood to absorb it. The blood turns into something not unlike soda water, causing excruciating pain and permanent injury. Of all the victims of the storm, those four men, trapped in their cramped chamber while their ship drifted towards possible shipwreck, must have been in the most uncomfortable situation.

In the Irish Sea, the Belfast to Heysham ferry *Spheroid* lost power for a time, and drifted towards the Manx coast, with Ramsay lifeboat in attendance. News of an Irish Sea ferry in difficulties, linked with the events in the south-east, raised memories of the last comparable storm, that of 1953, in which hundreds drowned on the east coast while the car ferry *Princess Victoria* foundered in the Irish Sea with 128 casualties after waves burst through her stern doors.

One other maritime emergency must also be recorded. Another Sealink ferry, the *Earl William*, had been pressed into an unusual service five months before. The Home Office had hired her to serve as a stationary detention ship for immigrants waiting for their claims to enter Britain to be heard. Immigrants' defence groups and the Harwich Maritime Association – which felt that the practice lowered the tone of the place – both pointed out that this function was uncomfortably reminiscent of the old prison-hulks of Dickens's day.

About half the 78 detainees aboard the *Earl William* were members of the Tamil minority from Sri Lanka. All summer a guerrilla war had been in progress in that beautiful island, involving increasingly savage terrorist reprisals and counter-reprisals between Tamils and Singhalese. At last the Sri Lanka government had invited the Indian army in to restore order, and its attempts to do so were just reaching their bloody climax in October.

With a degree of opportunism, large numbers of Tamils had converted their savings into air tickets, and arrived in Britain seeking entry as refugees, on the basis of a claim – which had some justification – that they might be in danger if they were sent back.

The Home Office had first of all staunched the inflow by providing that airlines must at their own expense carry future immigrants back to their countries of origin if they failed to gain entry. Then it had then played for time by decanting the Tamils into places of confinement like the *Earl William*, in the hope that the situation in Sri Lanka would resolve itself during the lengthy business of processing their applications, so that their claims to refugee status could be rejected.

Meanwhile the Tamils' friends and relations in this country mounted a spirited campaign in their support. A representative of the Seamen's Union came down to declare conditions on the ship unacceptable, journalists invoked the imagery of *Great Expectations*, and a ten-day hunger strike was organised. In August the chairman of the Tamil Action Committee, Mr Sinnappu Maharasingam, delivered a protest by hand to the Home Office, in which he made effective play with the poet Wordsworth's claim that England was become a fen of stagnant waters. In October he wrote to the chief of immigration officers, quoting Tennyson's observation to the effect that the old order changeth, giving place to new, lest one good custom should corrupt the world. The Government had reacted to his appeals with impassivity.

"It was a kind of torture for the detainees ", says Mr Maharasingam. "The paid staff looking after them were giving them stale food, I don't know why. They complained of severe pains. The cold weather brought out their inner insecurities. They always had the fear that the ship might be taken away into the sea. Every night a roll call was taken, and then they were locked into their cabins. They were in a state of collective fear."

Perhaps it was not quite as bad as that. Mr N.S. Kandasamy, one of the detainees, says that the private sector security men in charge of them were friendly, and only locked cabin doors at night when asked to. Television and newspapers were supplied. The detainees lent a hand in the canteen, and so were in a position to mitigate some of the rigours of English institutional cookery. But it must have been a boring and uncertain time for them, among the mud-flats in a wet English autumn, with little to do but wait for the slow-footed Home Office to make a move, and to scan the news for the latest reports on the Indian Army's slow progress in mopping up the Tamil Tigers, street by street through Jaffna.

Now at 5.30 am. the ship broke her mooring lines like the *Hengist* and drifted out into the Stour estuary. As the wind caught her, she heeled over and the crash of falling cutlery alarmed the inmates. "We heard a noise – the storm was very strong", says Mr Kandasamy. "Then it started sailing without anybody's control. They didn't tell us anything. 250 yards it sailed under nobody's control. One of the guards said just for a joke that you are all going to Colombo harbour."

"The scene was one of utter chaos", said Bob Bliss, a Trinity House representative at Harwich. "The lines all snapped one after another, ping, ping, ping, and there was nothing anybody could do about it. She dropped both her anchors – they didn't hold. Three tugs were trying to hold her, but they couldn't."

As the ship lurched away from the quay, she smashed into anchored yachts, sinking several, and hit a barge which left an 18-inch hole in her stern. "Some water came in, but the hole was above the waterline", said Colin Crawford, the port manager. Harbour board staff considered mounting a helicopter rescue for a time, but the ship grounded off Shotley instead of drifting out on the ebb tide like the heroic children in Arthur Ransome's *We Didn't Mean to Go to Sea*, and the plan was dropped.

Raised by telephone in London, Mr Maharasingam reacted much as Lord Marshall had in similar circumstances, though he is not a man formed by nature to chortle. He was on the line to the Home Office in a moment, and found it understandably in disarray.

"I said: 'This is what I predicted. Now I'm going to take them!'. They said: 'Please take them'. They agreed to give them temporary admission and allow them to live with relatives and genuine sponsors in the community.

"I believe that when human beings collectively cry, there is an answer. 'The furious hand of nature has come to the aid of the Tamils', I told *The Guardian*. I hired a coach from Harwich, and went to the ship. By that time it had been brought to moorings again.

"They were in a terrible state, but they were hilarious. They tried to catch me and carry me on their shoulders. Other nationalities came and shook my hand. They were transformed. I had seen them in dejection, thinking that everything was of no use. Now freedom was to come, and I saw a different face altogether."

There was a jubilant reception waiting for the exhausted party when they arrived at the Tamil temple in Wimbledon. It was a great day. The hurricane had blown the Home Office right off the map.

CHAPTER 16

FROM GRAVE TO CRADLE

"Several women in the City of London who were in travail,
or who fell into travail by the fright of the storm, were obliged
to run the risque of being delivered with such help as they had."
(Daniel Defoe: *The Storm*)

The jet of warm air flowed onwards, drawing behind it a wake of colder air from the north and west. As the wind in London and the south began to lose some of its intensity, the wind in East Anglia was still rising. The gale streamed out over Cambridgeshire, Suffolk and Norfolk. The very highest recorded gust it achieved anywhere on the English mainland was the 122 mph it touched at 5.24 am at Gorleston, close to Great Yarmouth. The Met Office calculated that it was statistically improbable that a gust of equal strength would recur there for at least two centuries. There may have been stronger gusts elsewhere, but at many weather stations the measuring equipment ran off mains electricity, and fell victim to power cuts just when its records would have been most interesting.

The storm killed two people north of the Thames. Mrs Sylvia Brown was an early-rising postwoman in Canvey Island, who was trapped for nearly three hours under a 40-foot poplar in her garden, and died five days later in hospital. Sidney Riches was a Norfolk farmer, who swerved to avoid a fallen tree on the A 10 near King's Lynn, and crashed into a lorry.

The wind played all the tricks we have grown familiar with, and if I list them more briefly now for the sake of the reader's patience, that is not because I underestimate the impression it made. In Chelmsford, Clacton, Ipswich, Norwich, Orford, Waxham, Yarmouth and all the other affected places north of London, the impact came as something fresh, direct and stunning, and not as a repetition of a tale already told.

In Bramford road, Ipswich, the brick gable end of John Paul's house was blown inwards at 7 am, and fell through the ceiling of his bedroom, inches from where he was standing. The family had retreated downstairs, and he had come back to collect his hat. "It did not seem frightening at the time, everything seemed to happen in slow motion", he told the *Ipswich Evening Star*.

Whole glass shopfronts were sucked out in Colchester. The roof of Ipswich bus garage blew off and landed on a row of double deckers. The grandstand at Foxhall stadium, Ipswich, was reduced to twisted ruins. In

Chelmsford, a man was taken to hospital with injuries sustained from being struck by a flying dustbin.

In Canvey Island, no fewer than 400 caravans were damaged or destroyed. Small boats at anchor in the east coast estuaries were given a mauling. In Clacton 100 people had to be moved to bed and breakfast accommodation after their homes were damaged. Essex firemen received 1,800 calls before breakfast alone, compared to a normal total of 50 for a whole day. Some 700,000 customers of Eastern Electricity woke to find their power cut off. Water supplies failed too in some rural areas, as pumping stations were left without power.

In Stowmarket, a 130-foot turkey oak blew down and fell just 15 feet from the bedroom where ten-month-old Megan McSloy was sleeping, demolishing a garage and leaving her father Peter reflecting, like so many others: "If it had fallen at a slightly different angle . . ."

The great cedars at Ickworth, the rich landscaped parkland at Blickling Hall and the avenue of 25 oaks at Felbrigg Hall, were a few of the number added to the toll of stately trees felled by the wind. Thousands more joined the list of more plebean tree casualties. Plantations around Thetford and Woodbridge were especially badly hit. So was the famous bird sanctuary at Minsmere in Suffolk, with its combination of deep woodland and marshes where the rare avocet nests.

In Wymondham, Norfolk, 2½-year-old Ruth Charles had crept into bed with her parents as their timber-framed house shuddered in the gale. "It's like jelly", she murmured as first light came.

"What do you mean ?", her mother Rosemary asked her.

"Its like jelly. Jelly in the sky".

The rotating top of Horsey windmill in north Norfolk, a few miles from the badly-damaged medieval Waxham Great Barn, was torn off and thrown into a nearby dyke. It was not retrieved until the end of January 1988. Billingford windmill, near Diss, lost part of its sails.

Many barns, grain-stores, stables and commercial greenhouses were left in ruins. They had often been left uninsured because of the cost of premiums. Tubular greenhouses covered with plastic sheeting proved especially vulnerable, as they had in the Channel Islands. 17,000 hens were killed or injured at a poultry house near Chelmsford which lost its roof. Grain store roofs were ripped off as far north as Peterborough.

The storm seems in its latter hours to have developed a decided taste for attacking the House of God. Churches south of London suffered, but did not receive treatment so rough as to suggest a grudge. But in the Ipswich area alone three chapels and one church were seriously damaged. The 800-year-old Newbourne Church, near Woodbridge, Suffolk, had its east wall blown out, with the stained glass window above the altar and the whole roof left trembling. Cransford Baptist Chapel, Framlingham, was demolished except for a single wall. Its pews were left standing in rows under the sky. In addition to these, Thelnetham Church, near Diss, had its roof assailed by no fewer than three fallen trees.

At Heydon Church, north Norfolk, a falling lime tree exposed the macabre sight of human bones entangled among its roots. "We went down there last night with a torch and a spade and felt more like bodysnatchers, to be honest with you", churchwarden John Aves told the *North Norfolk News* a few days later. "We saw the bones and just threw some earth over them".

But this kind of grisly curiosity was something the storm had already shown evidence of earlier in the night. At Chilham in Kent, too, bones were laid bare in the overthrow of trees whose roots had felt their way down into older interments. Bob Ogley records that at Crowborough, Sussex, gravestones in the town cemetery were lifted, headstones were smashed and crosses cracked.

Not that such events are so much out of the natural course of things. Every country parson is familiar with that tendency that bones in soil have to creep a little nearer heaven as the centuries pass, and the particles of soil gradually wash down past them. The same process will have been at work elsewhere since the storm, gradually packing the earth tightly again round the loosened roots of trees which were nearly overset.

The storm seems to have brought more rain with it in its later stages. Much of East Anglia, like much of the Weald, was already under an urgent flood alert. More than an inch of rain had fallen in many places north and south of the Thames in the previous 24 hours, and torrents more had been predicted. But while some reports from the Weald spoke of pouring rain, in most places the wind seems only to have carried a few stinging drops, and the expected floods held off for a few hours more.

But in East Anglia, as in the West Country, the first thrust of the storm brought heavy rain with it, and floods multiplied the difficulties of the emergency services. There was flooding in the Waveney, Gipping and Stour valleys, and 300 flood-threatened homes were evacuated at Jaywick, Clacton.

The storm careered on, over the Wash and out into the great emptiness of the North Sea. The centre of the depression, which was still very nearly as deep as it had been when it arrived over the mainland, crossed the east coast close to Hull as daylight came. The airflows pursuing it now formed a westerly flow over the whole southern half of the country. The wind was definitely past its peak, though still capable of gusts of nearly 70 mph.

The gale fell with almost equal severity on Belgium and Holland, though the wind there never rose higher than 80 mph except on the coast. There was widespread damage to buildings, and crops worth "many millions of guilders" were destroyed. A falling tree killed 32-year-old Niko Vriend, of Heiloo in Holland, and many people were injured. At Schipol airport, flying debris punched two holes in the hull of a Boeing 727, and a Boeing 737 standing on the tarmac "went berserk", and airport staff had to struggle to bring the 27-ton plane to a halt.

By 8 am the wind had dropped below gale force in all inland areas of England except East Anglia and around Cranwell in Lincolnshire. There were reports of a school in Sheffield which was damaged so badly that the pupils were sent home. Workmen on York Minster, 250 miles from the storm's first point of attack on the English mainland, spent most of the day securing scaffolding that winds were making unsafe. But these were only flourishes at the margin of the departing tempest.

The midlands and north had seen the barometer fall almost as low as the south had done. But they had experienced only moderate northerly winds, cruising down to rendezvous with the approaching low. The dynamics of the spinning vortex had never set up there the strong pressure contrasts which drew the air on the opposite side of the depression so impetuously forward.

Once the storm left the mainland, the temperature of the sea was still sufficiently mild to provide it with a fresh source of power, in the same way as the tropical sea can do to a flagging hurricane. By 7 pm the depression had deepened again to 954 millibars, slightly deeper than its lowest recorded level over the English mainland. The northern North Sea and the Norwegian coast endured a very severe gale. Meanwhile, another front was coming up across Biscay, faster than the weathermen had predicted. But for a few hours the weather allowed us a respite.

As people got over the first impression of shock, and reassured themselves of their own safety, they began, by a natural extension, to turn to see whether anyone else needed their help.

"In adversity you come closer", says Terry Buckley, whose home beside the beach at Seaford had been shaken half to pieces, as described in chapter 7. "About ten or twelve of us went out first thing to see how things were. We started to clear stuff away. There was a caravan lying on its side blocking the whole road, with wood and joists from the smashed roofs lying all round it. We used the joists to lever the van upright.

"Down the road we found terible damage. The one who'd had the narrowest escape was the man whose house the garage roof had hit [Mr Arthy]. He had gone downstairs to fetch a cup of tea, and just then the whole front of his room upstairs was smashed. Someone said they had seen whole bricks just flying and disintegrating like cardboard as they hit the wall.

"Lots of us were just going round reassuring people – a very strong community spirit came to the surface. Everybody was amazing. We knocked on one old dear's door to see if she was all right. She didn't answer, and we broke her window to see if anything had happened. We found her fast asleep – she had slept right through it.

"The electricity had gone, but some of us had gas facilities. We had a big extended breakfast in our house for about eight people."

Voluntary workers from the Red Cross, the Womens' Royal Voluntary Service and similar organisations were out and active as soon as they took the measure of the need. They were still handing out soup and comfort a week or more after the disaster, in some cases.

At Selsey, Sussex, where 300 caravans were damaged, the parish hall was opened in the small hours so that 120 refugees could shelter there. "They arrived in their night-clothes carrying their pet dogs and cats and budgies", said Mike Blaylock, chairman of the parish council. More than 50 men were sent into the Selsey area from the Royal Military Barracks at Chichester to help with the evacuation, after the 999 services appealed for help.

The chaos was a stimulus to other kinds of enterprise as well. Navigational and other equipment worth £1,800 was stripped from boats washed ashore at Bembridge in the Isle of Wight. Looters were out in the Holloway Road, north London. Allied Carpets in Southampton was thoroughly picked over after its frontage collapsed into the street. In the streets of Brighton and Worthing, covered with broken glass and spilled litter, looters darted from one broken window to another, snatching their chances while they could. They were helped in finding their way, perhaps, by the flashing of battery-powered burglar alarms, which had been set off by the buffetting of the wind – they were the only lighting that there was in many streets during the hours of the power cut.

The police did what they could to guard the shopping areas, but their resources were already overstretched. In Eastbourne, video equipment and compact disc players worth £3,000 were taken from Debenhams. At the Army and Navy Stores in Hove, Ted Jones, the 70-year-old caretaker, could only stand and watch as thieves strolled in and out with armfuls of glass, porcelain and bronze goods worth thousands of pounds. "He was on his own and there was little he could do – we told him not to try to tackle them", said William Welstead, the manager.

Some of the helpers in those hours were volunteers, some were only doing their job. I have already had much to say about the police, fire and ambulance services. Across the territories of about fifty principal local authorities and hundreds of subsidiary ones, the seldom-tested machinery of emergency went into action with an efficiency which deserved all the praise which was quickly lavished on it, and as quickly forgotten.

"We have a cascade system of getting hold of people", says Eric Wilcock, emergency planning officer for Kent. "I have a team of about 30. Everyone has a list of people to get in touch with, designed to ensure that the message goes round as far as possible, even if there are communications failures. Each section has its own defined responsibilities to get on with. Once the system is activated you don't stop until someone with the authority tells you to.

"The county is the highway authority, so our initial problem was very much highway-related. Every single road in Kent was blocked, to begin with. But it didn't stop there. People were in trouble, so it became a social services problem, too. One of our principles is that counties and districts get on with their defined roles. The job of the emergency centre is to collate information. The main responsibility is naturally given to those who normally manage each job. We define priorities, they manage their own affairs.

"Exactly a year ago we had a fairly big test exercise. Then there was the snow in the spring – and then the *Herald of Free Enterprise* affair. So we were fairly well rehearsed.

"The county surveyor and his staff got stuck in, borrowing staff from other departments – property services, groundsmen – to help clear the main roads. By degrees other problems were identified – electricity supply . . . sewage . . . We ended by moving generators around the county to keep the pumping stations going. Supplies department knew where to get them and the military could help there, too.

"It was the districts' job to handle people who had to be evacuated because their homes were untenable, and to open up rest centres. They came to us for supplies and stores – tarpaulins, for instance.

"Then there was the political side. By now we could see we were into the business of spending millions. We had to 'manage the political scene', get onto the government, find out what the resources situation might be. Our politicians were very helpful.

"I was in contact with the chief executive at 6 am. The first decision we had to take was whether to close the schools. It was patently obvious it would be dangerous to allow children to go out in those conditions. The police were concurrently advising people to stay off the streets, which reinforced our decision.

"That message was passed to Radio Kent, one of the earliest contacts on our list."

Radio contact was among the first preoccupations of Sevenoaks District Council, too, when its emergency team met at 8 am. With only two out of their 40 telephone lines operating, their ability to control events depended largely on the amateur radio group, Raynet. Their volunteers installed themselves in the corner of the operations room and climbed to the roof to point their aerial and establish contact with Eric Wilcock at his headquarters in Maidstone, the county town.

Bruce Cova, chief executive of Sevenoaks, told his team that the day's conditions were the nearest to nuclear war that he hoped they would ever see. His council had a total staff of 500, including only six experienced foresters, and they had an area of 300 square miles to cover, with 900 miles of road to clear. The borough of Camden in London, by contrast, covers 24 square miles and has 10,000 staff.

"We had no communications, no power, and at one stage, no petrol", he told *The Observer*. "When we run practice courses for the next war, we assume we'd send people out to get things done before the fall-out. The fact is, you're not going to get anyone out there . . . it's pointless talking about liaison with the county or anyone else."

The storm was local radio's finest hour. With telephone lines down and power cuts making most television sets useless, it enabled the authorities to send out emergency messages to thousands of households which had battery sets. Radio Invicta in Maidstone sent out the council's message about the closure of schools, passed on the Electricity Board's warnings about the dangers of fallen live power cables, and transmitted an appeal from Canterbury police for the loan of chainsaws.

But when Radio Invicta's early shift arrived at the station at 4 am, it was touch and go whether there would be any transmissions at all. It took them 40 minutes, working by the light of car headlights, to kick their reluctant emergency generator into life. Reporters struggled for miles across country to send reports of conditions in coastal towns. The station's own telephone lines were still working, so that it could receive news reports and calls from the public.

With the disruption of telephone services, the transmission of urgent private and public messages often depended on local radio or the police. Mr and Mrs Doddington of Bexhill had to wait until mid-morning wondering whether 60 guests were about to descend on their roofless house for the planned wedding reception. Mrs Doddington, who is not one to give up easily, spent the morning working out how to transfer the reception to the church hall down the road – "I *would* have managed". But eventually a message was passed through from Dorking to say that their daughter had called off the wedding reception. Marion came to Bexhill anyway on the Saturday, with the rest of the family, to help her parents clear up.

So many people were turning out to offer help in these hours that it is almost invidious to be specific. I happened to telephone Thanet District Hospital, because I had heard that a ward had been evacuated because of structural damage. Yes, it had, Geoff Rebbeck, the hospital administrator, told me. The flat roof of a geriatric orthopaedic ward had lifted in the wind, and in the morning thirteen beds were evacuated, because the roof was no longer waterproof. The roof of a block of staff residences had flown off completely, and half of it landed 30 yards away.

"One of the building artisan staff picked up a panel of wood in the special care nursery, to put in a broken window. The wind wrenched it out of his hand and bashed him on the head. He had to go for treatment – but afterwards he came straight back to work: that shows the spirit there was.

" We have 50 land telephone lines to the hospital, but they were all lost, and we couldn't even make local calls. Our casualty department is usually closed at night, but we reopened it to deal with about 25 cases of contusions and shock, and one heart attack not directly related to the storm. Nothing too serious. A lot of off-duty staff, the ones who lived within walking distance, started coming in from 4 am onwards to see if they could help".

Everyday stories of a unique day. There must have been thousands of people whose first impulse as soon as they dared to leave their homes was to get out and help someone.

The pattern of emergency provision in Britain is a diffused one, dependent on the initiative of a great many people rather than a strict hierarchy of command. In a diffused, low-technology catastrophe like the storm, this system worked well – although it was much debated afterwards whether it would have responded as well to other kinds of disaster.

For one group of those caught up in the storm, it was a special day in more senses than one – the expectant mothers, four of whom we left counting their contractions four chapters ago.

Towards 4 am, Julie and John Pell had dodged their way home to Cowden, near Tunbridge Wells, from their stranded car, which they had abandoned in the attempt to reach Pembury maternity hospital. By now, Mrs Pell was in the second stage of labour. After urgent telephone calls, a doctor was found to come to their aid from Edenbridge, three miles away. He too had to leave his car and scramble over fallen trees to reach their home. There he presided over the arrival of Andrea Pell at 11 am.

Marilyn Price, a couple of miles away in Blackham, was having a more difficult labour. During the morning Pembury Hospital decided to call for the aid of a helicopter. The pilot found a landing-place clear of trees, and flew her from her cottage to a playing-field near the hospital, where an ambulance was waiting. Her son Simon hesitated until the evening before consenting to venture out into a world turned upside-down.

By 5.30 am Elizabeth Elliott-Noye in Bexhill was in a good deal of pain and feeling increasingly panicky. Her husband Bill rang the police again. They were reassuring and promised to send a radio call to the ambulance station, only five minutes drive away. But the ambulance took half an hour to arrive. They had found two roads blocked and had got through only at the third attempt.

"They could not get to the house because there were fallen trees all over the place, so they took me on a stretcher through a gap in the fence where it had been blown away and through our neighbours' garden", says Mrs Elliott-Noye. "The ambulance man told me he had just seen somebody's greenhouse just floating through the air, like something out of Mary Poppins.

"It usually only takes about 15 minutes in busy traffic to get to the hospital in Hastings, but it took us three-quarters of an hour, driving over the trees and up onto the pavements. Bill was following us in the car.

"We arrived at the hospital at about 6.45. It was so busy that they had to take a woman off a bed in the delivery room who was not so advanced in labour."

But it was found that the baby was going to need a forceps delivery. The consultant had to be called in from Battle. It was less than five miles away, but he too was cut off and had to set out on foot, trying to thumb a lift as he went. It was another hour before he arrived and successfully delivered 7lb 14½oz Rebecca, the Elliott-Noyes' first child.

Frances Esposito in Ardingley slept soundly until half past six. Then she stirred, and asked her husband Claude to get their two sons dressed and take them in the car to some friends who had offered to look after them while the baby was coming. He drove off, but was soon back: the road to Balcombe was impossible to get through.

"Even then I wasn't bothered: I just said 'Oh, that doesn't stop us getting through to Crawley'. But Claude went off to have a word with the village policeman, who told him that all five roads out of Ardingley were blocked. The police station's telephones were dead, and he could not get a message out either.

"On the way back, Claude saw a gentleman with a citizen's band radio, and thought of asking him if he could get a message out to Crawley Hospital. He said he'd try, and he added that his wife knew a midwife who lived in the village – we didn't know there was one."

When Mr Esposito came triumphantly home with the bad news and the good news, and with a real live midwife in tow, his wife was troubled, because she did not think she needed a midwife for ages yet. But the midwife, Mrs Margaret Dale, examined her and found that she was already nearly nine centimetres dilated, which meant that the baby was soon going to arrive. Another neighbour, a nurse, and her husband, a community physician, stood by ready to help, as did Peter Edgeler, the policeman.

Mrs Dale had no stethoscope, and listened through the cardboard centre of a toilet roll to see whether the baby was in distress. "I pressed it against the mother's tummy and I could hear the heartbeats", she said. "It was all the equipment we had".

Mrs Esposito was distantly aware of a trainee GP turning up at some stage too, raising the qualified personnel present to four. Meanwhile the story of the baby was humming through the local ether, as police radio operators tried to locate an ambulance and road-clearing vehicles which might have a chance of breaking through into the village. Illicit monitors of the police radio bands registered that a good story was in progress in Ardingley, and soon the local press were in hot pursuit.

"It all worked by Chinese whispers, I think. There was all this melée of people outside turning up to help – about 30 people asking what they could do. The men sat downstairs. But up in the room it was a haven of tranquillity. It was a beautiful birth – not particularly easy, but not hard. The midwife was exceptionally professional. She didn't allow any of her natural concern to relay itself to me. She went out once to tell them to alert the hospital that the baby was coming, but she pretended to me that she was only going to the loo.

"The baby arrived at 10.45. Literally five minutes after he was born, an ambulance, a fire engine, a tender in case it broke down, and a breakdown vehicle, too, all arrived outside. Suddenly there were 14 people in my bedroom – ambulance-men, policemen, friends . . . all glad and all of them congratulating us.

"The baby weighed nine pounds two ounces, and we called him Petr. I have to say I was sad it wasn't a daughter. But the way it happened did make it a very special birth. I know that day was a dark one for many other people, but it was a happy one for us".

CHAPTER 17

THE MORNING AFTER

*"If it was the wind", said Owl, considering the matter, "then
it wasn't Pooh's fault. No blame can be attached to him."*
(A. A. Milne: *The House at Pooh Corner*)

Most of us had had a fair night's sleep. Some did not realise that anything
really out of the way had happened until they stepped outdoors, and found
the landscape transformed.

"I came round the corner, and the trees were just lying flat. I was walking down the street not knowing whether to laugh or cry, and people were
half with tears in their eyes and half giggling", says Joan Curtis, a painter
and partwork editor in Barnes, south London.

Even on board the *Malcolm Miller*, one of the schooner's young trainees
slept through all the night's alarms and came on deck rubbing his eyes and
muttering: "Is something happening?"

Some people woke to find that horrible tricks had been played on them.
The staff of the Brighton Pavilion stared in disbelief at the stone, the size of
a dustbin, which lay half-buried in the middle of their brand-new blue and
gold carpet. The Dean of Chichester, the Very Reverend Robert Holtby,
walked round his cathedral to inspect the ravages of the night, and found
that stained glass had been smashed and a pinnacle from the tower had fallen
into a side-aisle of the nave, close to the medieval stone screen. "What
appeared to be a boulder, rather like an object from outer space, had come
in through the triforium roof, where there was great hole", he said.

The Reverend Alyn Owens, vicar of St Luke's United Reform Church,
St Leonards, was called to his church by a telephone call to find the spire
crammed like a dunce's cap into a ruined side chapel. "It looks as if it will
cost about £100,000 to replace", he said later. "A lot of people in the
church say don't replace it, that it's never been anything but trouble. People
outside the church are saying you can't put it up without a spire. It's an aesthetic decision really".

I tried to provoke both churchmen into reflections on the concept of an
Act of God, which would certainly have perplexed their predecessors in
Defoe's time. But they were not to be drawn. "The events arose out of the
operations of nature, and there was no more significance in the events of the
night than in any other natural accident", said the Dean rather curtly.

"I am not really reflective about Acts of God" said Mr Owens. "I haven't actually taken up that theme in the pulpit, though I might when we re-dedicate the church, and I can put it into the context of our not being beaten and winning through. When God created the world all was dull and void and creativity came in the midst of chaos. But chaos still lingers – the uncontrollable part of nature – and it's up to us to show we're not beaten".

This is perhaps the only area in which comparison between Defoe and the reactions of witnesses in 1987 does not create a strong impression of the consistency of human nature. Defoe and his correspondents expatiated with a good deal of solemn glee on the moral lessons to be drawn from the affliction which had been visited on the nation. In 1987 a certain intuitive sense of awe was apparent in the reactions of those who had narrow escapes when trees or chimneys came down. Those who lived to tell the tale felt that some special providence had protected them, without inquiring very deeply into what implications might follow. Those who did not were in no position to do so, of course.

It is understandable that churchmen treat these issues warily. That side of things expressed by the psalmist's words about the cedars of Lebanon skipping like a young unicorn, or Gerard Manley Hopkins's line about "the dark side of the bay of His blessing" is a mysterious issue to handle, and some clergymen prefer to regard disaster as among the subjects which have been relinquished to the civil power. But the hell-fire sermon makers of the past would have felt that opportunities were being lost here.

The sculptor Antony Gormley had a more personal blow. He was off first thing to see how his new studio in Peckham had fared, to find most of the window panes gone. After breakfast he set out on his bike for the other studio in Brixton where his work was still stored, and it was only as he cycled through the confusion that it occurred to him to wonder what might have happened there.

"Halfway there it suddenly dawned that if that big wall was ever likely to come down, it would have done last night. The studio is one of a row backing onto the wall of a demolished storage warehouse, a high brick wall which was left when the warehouse was taken down.

"Immediately I arrived I was met by a sculptor called Matthew Parry, who said 'I advise you not to go any further'. He was fairly speechless. But I went down, and the top 15 feet of the wall had collapsed into my studio."

Mr Gormley had 19 pieces there in all, representing about a year and a half's work. There had been an exhibition at the Serpentine Gallery, and plans were well advanced for an exhibition in New York. Insofar as such things can be priced in the abstract, their current value would have run into several hundred thousand pounds.

They were life-size human figures, made of lead applied to the surface of thin moulds that had been taken from the living body, mostly from his own, and reinforced inwardly with fibreglass. They are in effect full-length life masks. Their interest for Gormley is not so much as portraits, but as records defining the space once occupied by a living body. The colour and associations of the lead give them a faintly macabre presence: not life mask so much as death mask, or sarcophagus.

"As I carried the damaged pieces out of the ruins I felt I was reliving some sort of postwar atrocity – the kind of scenes you see in Enniskillen or Beirut. Many of the finished pieces I'd kept because they still retained sources of energy I had not fully tapped. I hadn't got to the end of my relationship with them, and I'm still haunted by them. One of the figures was more or less unscathed, one was repairable – the rest not. Everything there was finished work. Sculpture isn't something you do piecemeal – if I tried to re-make the shoulder or side of a figure, the chances are I'd end up reworking the whole.

"I cried a lot, that day. It has made me think a lot. I regard the whole event as being in a sense nature pruning the works of man. There are times when I feel it was strangely appropriate, I don't know why. One whole aspect of my work has been to reposition man within a kind of elemental context. I will have to make some works which deal with the thoughts and feelings bound up in those sculptures, and what happened to them".

A peculiar smell hung over southern England as it grew light – fresh and sharp, unforgettable – a little like a cut apple. It was the smell of broken trees, of mashed and shredded leaves and branches, sap, bark, and resin. It was soon accompanied by another smell and another sound, both of which were to be in the nostrils and the ears for many days to come – the shriek of the chainsaw and the more aromatic fragrance of newly-cut timber.

The morning seemed a most beautiful one. In terms of cold statistics, there was nothing so special about it: the sunshine was intermittent, the wind was still cutting enough to take your eyebrows off and the temperature was seven degrees lower than it had been in the middle of the night. But there was a palpable sense of relief, strangeness, light-headedness – which I am sure was connected with some sort of physiological response to the sharp changes of pressure we had experienced (though doctors insist that these were minimal compared to what one experiences walking up a fell, or making a journey by air).

It was the kind of morning which must have made many people think of man "within an elemental context", if they had time to pause to think at all. Act of God or not, the works of man were in disarray on a stupendous scale. London was an island in an ocean of inaccessibility. Commuting was to be pioneering this morning.

The social organism between Portland and King's Lynn had come virtually to a halt. The ordinary means of communication were largely defunct over most of the most prosperous and populous third of England, a territory with 17 million inhabitants. At the peak of the power cuts early in the morning, three million households and businesses were cut off. More than a million would still be without power by the evening, and more than 400,000 three days afterwards. About 150,000 telephone subscribers were cut off, of whom just over half would still be cut off a week later.

Thousands of homes, hundreds of villages, and at least one large town – Sevenoaks – were wholly cut off by road. Kent police reported that 90 per cent of all roads in the county were blocked. Part of the M4 motorway was closed, which made it almost impossible to approach London by car from the west.

In London itself, hardly a street was without its fallen dinosaur of a tree, and its crushed beetle of a car. Most schools were closed, though not so much because of damage as to avoid bringing children out onto the roads: all but 26 in inner London were open again on Monday. Scotland Yard took twice its normal daily number of emergency calls in the few hours of the storm. The fire brigade took 6,000 emergency calls in 24 hours, twice its previous maximum and sixteen times its normal daily total. London had not suffered a blow like it since the Second World War.

The huge machinery of road and rail which normally decants more than half a million commuters into London from the southern counties every weekday morning had stopped. No trains at all ran on the Southern Region that morning. It was two days before trains were able to leave Liverpool Street or Fenchurch Street to serve Essex, Cambridge and East Anglia. Even by the evening, the London Underground was still able to operate only at two-thirds efficiency. Lines from Victoria to the south coast were open only as far as Purley by evening, and from Charing Cross only as far as Kidbrooke and Orpington.

The main line to London just south of Rochester was invisible beneath a quarter-mile long blanket of fallen oaks. Between Tunbridge Wells and Battle, 300 trees had fallen across the double track, an average of ten trees to the mile. Trains to the west and south-west were less affected, with the Waterloo–Weymouth line and the Paddington–Bristol service both working. The 1 am service from Victoria to Gatwick had been stopped by a fallen tree near Merstham in Surrey. In a story which gives a clue to the kind of chaos there would have been if the storm had arrived when crowds were on the move, Bob Ogley describes how the frightened passengers had to wait two hours before an engine came to shunt them to the station. But it had scarcely begun to do so when it, too, was damaged by falling trees. The passengers had to stumble along the track to the station, hardly daring to look up at the trees tossing overhead. They waited at Merstham until 4 am, when a train took them to Redhill, where they were given shelter and a cup of tea in a canteen. But the electricity failed, and they were shepherded back onto the train and spent the rest of the night there.

5,000 trees had to be cleared from Southern Region lines, and 2,000 from Eastern Region ones. It was estimated that it would cost the Southern region alone up to £2 million to repair the night's damage. A policy decision was taken to allow season-ticket holders an extra day's validity if the gale had wiped their journeys out.

Even when the trees had been hoisted away from the lines, it was found that the masses of leaves on the rails made trains' wheels slip. Longer trains were found to ride over the sodden leaf-mould with more momentum, and services had to be rewritten so that trains big enough to get through could be assembled.

Airports were less badly affected. Heathrow and Gatwick were both in action by 7.30 am, though debris had to be cleared from the runways and services were restricted. Light planes at Biggin Hill and Shoreham had been flipped onto their backs and tossed on top of one another.

As for cars, they had been slaughtered in hecatombs in town and country. Images of contorted steelwork and gleaming chrome buried in leaves and borne down by gnarled branches were as familiar a part of the iconography of the storm as images of the trees themselves. Lorries on exposed roads had been tipped onto their sides. The Association of British Insurers estimated that claims under motor policies connected with the storm amounted to £25 million. Many drivers do not insure their cars except for the third-party risks required by law, so the actual total of loss must have been much higher.

There were some who felt more grief over the sufferings of their cars than anything else. "Bodywork attacked by taloned houri" noted John Crocker of Seaford, after coming down from a roofless flat to inspect damage to the apple of his eye. Many of the innumerable anecdotes of the storm which immediately began to proliferate dealt with the griefs and ironies of car ownership. These tales had some of the character of urban myth; it became hard to determine whether they were representative tragedies which really happened, or whether they were things which everyone felt should have happened, and attributed to a friend of a friend. Some may have happened many times over.

One owner (or scores, or none) had seen that the wind was getting up, and had conscientiously gone out in pyjamas and raincoat to move his car under cover, only to find in the morning that the garage had been demolished, and the space on the driveway had not been touched. Another owner had taken comfort from the knowledge that his two cars were many miles apart: both were flattened. Another owned two cars, one of which was a Porsche; naturally, the falling tree singled out the Porsche and left the other unscathed.

I secured first-hand confirmation of one tale which initially I would have been prepared to bet on being merely *ben trovato* – the story of the parking-slot poacher's come-uppance. When David Sore, a clerk in a City solicitors' office, arrived home in Tooting the night before the storm, he was vexed to see a neighbour dodging into his favourite parking-place. "We don't really get on – its just one of those things – and this time, just as I was about to park my Fiesta, he nipped in. In the morning I looked out: he had ended up with a tree on his car – it was a complete write-off".

By 9 am most of the main roads in Inner London had been cleared by council workers at least for single-lane traffic. The JCBs had broken the back of the work on Highgate Road by then, when I walked out to see what was left of Hampstead Heath. A tree had come down a few yards from the bus shelter where Yorkie, a jovial white-whiskered vagrant, has lived for years in a nest of cardboard boxes and placards reading: 'Social Security Burks Keep Off'.

"Slept through it – never heard it fall!'', he declared triumphantly in his squeaky voice.

The row of 'bobble-hanging planes' nearby, which caught the dreamy eye of the child John Betjeman as he rode the tram home to Highgate, and later appeared in his poem *Parliament Hill Fields*, had all survived unscathed. But a dozen trees in the avenue which runs from Well Walk towards the prehistoric tumulus had come down on one another like dominoes. The Heath was so much changed that my wife found herself virtually lost after taking only a few steps onto it. The steel panel on Parliament Hill which explains the panorama of the city spread out below had been made obsolete overnight with the disappearance of trees depicted in its foreground.

The willows beside the Highgate Ponds were in a miserable state, thrashing shattered boughs in the gale and the cold sunshine. On the boating pond, a solitary model yacht, the three-masted *Thermopylae*, was plunging to and fro at speed under reefed topsails. "The wind will come across the water better now those trees are down'', said the model's vicarious skipper with relentless satisfaction.

Oddly enough, he was not the only user of the Heath to react in this way. Christopher Ikin, who has studied the Heath and its history closely, declared afterwards that the storm had done good work in clearing it of much unduly regimented and park-like planting, which everyone had been too sentimental to do away with. It is true that the Heath has changed almost out of recognition since Constable painted it in the 1820s, turning from a heath into a public garden.

An energetic controversy ensued: not the least important of the Heath's recreational services to the people of Hampstead is the opportunities it offers them for exercise of this kind.

Car or no car, train or no train, innumerable commuters set out for the office in accordance with duty or habit. Some set off on foot while it was still dark, some made wide sweeps across country on buses that happened to be going somewhere vaguely connected with their destination, or begged a lift from the milkman.

Those who were about in the City speak of an uncanny hush in the litter-strewn streets under the darkened office-blocks. No traffic, but only the footsteps of innumerable weary pilgrims in pin-stripes and bowlers, greeting each other in low tones of subdued heroism, asking after the fate of each other's homes, laconically dropping tales of bread vans and detours via unheard-of tracts of the East End. Echoes of the blitz.

It was reported that the Stock Exchange was closed for the first time since the devaluation of the pound in 1974, or alternatively that dealers tired of looking at blank screens which had ceased to glow (finally, as it turned out) with the luminous promises of the longest, loftiest world bull market in history, had eventually been drawn downstairs to the trading floor. It had swiftly been deserted after the "Big Bang" deregulation a year earlier. There they had begun doing deals face to face, as their fathers had.

This last has all the ingredients of urban myth. Many who told the story would have liked it to happen. They would have been glad for the slick new world of yuppie finance to have been confounded for once by an act of nature. The Stock Exchange maintains officially that a myth is all it was. The electronic systems were not working at first and had to be "kick-started". By 10 am they were up and running, and business was done. There cannot have been much, because relatively few traders had fought their way in from the ravaged stockbroker belt. The day's deals were reported on a "best endeavours" basis and listed among the next Monday's transactions. But except for the section of the old trading floor which regularly houses the options market, no trading was done down there.

Those who wish may still suppose that this was only a political denial, like Dover's "We never closed" in chapter fifteen. It is hard to prove a negative: perhaps a deal or two was struck on the floor while the Stock Exchange was not looking.

The Bank of England makes no bones about having shut down major parts of its operation. Power lines were down, communications were in disarray: at 10 am it announced that it would not be buying or selling bills or issuing stock. An hour later, another announcement that there would be no settlements that day effectively turned Friday into a Bank Holiday – a day which did not exist as far as house purchase, the exchange of stocks and the clearing of cheques were concerned.

There turned out to be a certain poignancy about these City events, because they were acted out unwittingly under the shadow of a worldwide financial calamity to which our gale is no more than a footnote. Friday's dealing in other centres showed the first signs of falling confidence which portended the disasters of Black Monday – the day when world markets fell more violently than they had done even in the crash of 1929. The paper value written off shares worldwide was said to have been no less than a trillion pounds (a million million) – a stupendous amount to have been swept away to oblivion on the wind. It seemed possible that the world stood on the brink of a second slump.

In retrospect, the convulsion in the heavens and the convulsion in the markets must have merged together in the imaginations of many afflicted City gents, with the crash of the trees and the crash in prices reverberating as one. It must have been in some such spirit that the most studied joke of the week was constructed. The urban legend of 1929 is that there were mass suicides by ruined financiers throwing themselves out of Wall Street skyscrapers. But on Black Monday a double stroke of good fortune prevented this, the joke ran. Yuppies seeking to throw themselves out of skyscrapers were frustrated by the permanently-sealed windows which go with air-conditioning. They rushed to Hampstead Heath to hang themselves from a tree, only to find none still standing.

Like many black jokes, this one was only marginally blacker than real life: there were a number of suicides connected with Black Monday, in the USA at least, and at least one in Britain connected with the storm. Lord De La Warr was the owner of Ashdown Forest in Kent, the sandy territory in which A. A. Milne set his stories about Pooh Bear. It contained the tree Owl lived in, which was blown down on the Blusterous day; and Galleons Lap, a hilltop where in Christopher Robin's day there were "sixty-something trees in a circle", the number of which one could never exactly count: fewer since the storm, no doubt.

To save the estate intact, a complicated sale to the local authority was being negotiated. Lord De La Warr was greatly oppressed by his responsibilities, and was already under treatment for depression. A few days after the storm, he fell onto the rails under an Underground train. The storm was cited at his inquest as a contributory factor in his death. Two Breton farmers ruined by the storm were also reported to have killed themselves.

The law courts were as much in disarray as the City. In the High Court there were few cases in which judges, barristers, juries and witnesses had all managed to make it to the court at once. Of the 54 cases set down for hearing, only 19 were heard. Fears for the tall green dome of the Central Criminal Court stopped proceedings there in all but one of its courts.

Politicians reacted to the emergency with commendable swiftness, appreciating instantly the importance of being seen to be doing something. There was none of the august deliberation of Government ministers in France, who let the weekend go by before meeting to show how seriously they were taking things. But British ministers were in slight difficulties about what they should be seen to be doing, because Mrs Thatcher was abroad and not there to tell them. The Home Secretary, Mr Douglas Hurd, telephoned her for instructions.

Peter Bottomley, a junior transport minister, turned up on his own initiative to appear on Radio Four at 8 am and advise everyone to stay off the roads unless their journeys were absolutely necessary. This echoed the advice the police were giving. Hundreds of thousands gladly took it. However, the Confederation of British Industry, also under the imperative to make a distinctive contribution to the day's public statements, regretted that people had not shown more of the blitz spirit in fighting their way to work, and declared that "it wasn't an earthquake".

Maidstone Health Authority was so impressed by the CBI's argument that it announced that employees who "took the easy way out" and followed Mr Bottomley's advice to stay at home would lose a day's pay.

Cabinet Ministers held an emergency meeting in the morning, at which the departments of trade, transport, agriculture, energy, defence, local government – and of course the Treasury – were represented. Mr Hurd presided and afterwards called a press conference to say a few vague but reassuring things. He was also courageous enough to put in a word of comfort to the unhappy Met Office, which was in serious danger by now of being collectively lynched for not having forecast the storm.

The Opposition called for a State of Emergency to be declared, and Mr Hurd replied that things seemed to be going along quite satisfactorily without one. This was true enough: in fact, there was not very much that the Government needed to do at all until the question was faced of how the whole thing was to be paid for.

In the meantime, Nicholas Ridley, the Environment Secretary and a man of the soil, made arrangements to keep up the necessary image of activity by being pictured planting trees in parks. He appeared wielding a chain-saw in Richmond Park, in a city suit without any protective gear apart from ear-muffs, to set an example to the armies of relief workers in the Home Counties.

The press, true to type, reacted to the storm with shock and horror, started half a dozen quite fallacious hares and a couple of worthwhile ones, and poured out floods of precious circumstantial detail without which this book would have been a non-starter. *The Sun* filled its front page with a starlet who had been lucky enough to have her car flattened; the Communist *Morning Star* led with the Stakhanovite headline: "Hero Workers Triumph over Killer Storm".

Scarcely any publication, national or local, failed to refer to the blitz or to the way adversity brought out the best in the British character.

Numerous British characters were out on the roads at an early hour offering to patch roofs and cut trees at unheard-of-rates, and the newspapers were full of warnings to householders not to hand over their life savings to cowboys. Columnists implored the chainsaw infantry not to chop trees into such small pieces that the timber would be rendered unusable. This was all good advice, but widely disregarded. An urgent environmentalist lobby beseeched owners to leave a few of their dead trees on the ground for beetles to roost in: advice received sardonically by owners, many of them at a loss to see how they could afford even to open up their driveways.

Astronomical figures were hazarded as to the statistics of the disaster, most of which proved eventually to be a shadow of the truth. The country was stunned to learn that it had been bereaved of a million trees (15 million was the true number). Share prices of major insurance companies dropped sharply at suggestions that claims for the night's work might reach £300 million (£835 million is a conservative estimate of the actual figure).

The Met Office had immediately been appointed Britain's scapegoat for the disaster. "Why Weren't We Warned?" screamed the *Mail*. "Met men fail to predict" lamented *The Daily Telegraph*. "Wasted Warnings of the Storm" scolded *The Times*, launching the theme that Continental forecasters' better predictions had been disregarded. "Government to meet storm bill" carolled *The Independent*, prematurely.

The Met Office itself had had its telephone contact with the outside world completely severed, which hampered it in mounting an initial defence. Its television front-men were besieged by reporters at their homes. "The Met Office said there would not be a hurricane, and there was no hurricane", Dr John Houghton, the director-general, declared in an interview. This was true as far as it went, but created an unfortunate impression of pedantry. The last thing the nation wanted at that stage was to have its hurricane snatched away.

It was only after time for reflection that we began to wonder how much help it would have been to have been forewarned. Unlike the USA, England has no established refuges and codes of practice for coping with hurricanes. Many brave souls might have hastened out to make sure granny was all right, or simply to experience the storm of the century. The lost trees could not have been saved with tent pegs and string. If the storm had struck while the nation was still awake, the casualties would have been incalculably greater; perhaps we were all better off asleep.

Within hours, the hurricane was challenged in the headlines by more excesses of meteorology. The predicted rain held off only until the evening, and then began to fall in huge quantities, and without respite. Over the next few days, the rain sought out all the unsound roofs and fractured walls in the area of wind damage, and sent floods up to six feet feet deep streaming through areas which had escaped the first wave of attack. The west coast as far north as Cumbria was disrupted almost as completely as the south still was. Over two inches of rain fell in Wales on Monday night. Six of the staff of Carmarthen telephone exchange had to retreat to its roof, and were rescued from there by helicopter.

Terry Buckley in Seaford noticed a dripping sound in his ravaged bedroom, looked into the wall-unit and found a half-inch gap between one wall and the next, with water seeping through. The borough surveyor took one glance at it, declared the house an unsafe structure, and sent the family in search of a temporary home for weeks to come, like many more.

More than an inch of rain fell on the Home Counties in a day, and The Mall was closed by streams alleged in print to have been three feet deep, though this seems hard to credit. A perpetual twilight hung over the capital for days on end. The skipper of a lobster boat was lost when it capsized at the mouth of Chichester Harbour; a climber was drowned near Aber Falls in North Wales; and a driver in Oxfordshire was killed when her car fell into the swollen river Cherwell after colliding with a lorry.

The worst single accident of the entire history of the October storms happened early on Monday morning, when the 5.25 am train from Swansea to Shrewsbury drove onto a bridge at Manordilo, Dyfed, which had given way under floods a few minutes before. The front part of the two-carriage train plunged into the swollen river Tywi. Four people died, the driver and three passengers. One of them was 14-year-old Simon Penny from Swansea, who was on his way to school and went into the flood-water in an attempt to rescue disabled Mr Ben Evans and his wife Pat, who were riding in the front carriage. All three were drowned.

The track itself had not gone down when the bridge fell, so that the driver had not realised until the last moment that he was approaching a stretch of rails which had no bridge to support them. The train, the first of the day, had been carrying out an inspection of the track to make sure it was clear, after earlier reports that it had been flooded. An inspector and a manager were travelling on board to see what conditions were like.

The collapse of the 130-year-old bridge was a very unusual accident. But the whole procedure of using a passenger train to see whether a line is safe for running passenger services bears an uncomfortably close resemblance to the procedure of climbing out onto the branch of a tree as a convenient perch for cutting it off.

The response to the storms provided many examples of imagination and initiative. In the year of the loss of the *Herald of Free Enterprise* and the fire at King's Cross, it is perhaps wrong to be surprised that the storms too gave rise to one example of the same drowsy British adherence to routine which had characterised those other disasters.

CHAPTER 18

RESOLUTION AND INDEPENDENCE

"The ashes of an Oak in the Chimney are no epitaph of that
Oak to tell me how high or how large that was; It tells me not
what flocks it sheltered while it stood, nor what men it hurt when it fell."
(John Donne: *Sermons*)

In London, London seemed hard hit. But it was out of town that the real drama was taking place. Out in the wilderness, the man with a chain saw was a prince, and the man with a JCB was a king. The JCB – the initials are those of its manufacturer, J. C. Bamford – was the workhorse of the reconquest of the Weald, and a principal actor in most of the important scenes of the next few days.

It is a kind of Swiss Army Knife on wheels, a tractor equipped with shovel, 3-ton crane and innumerable smaller gadgets, undoubtedly including one for getting pebbles out of horses' hooves. It appears that in the spirit of the first masterpiece of Henry Ford, it can be ordered in any colour the customer fancies, so long as it is canary-yellow. People were ready to sell their souls for a JCB in those days, and householders with trees sprawling all over their property would stand at their gates brandishing ten-pound notes, hoping to waylay a passing JCB just for an hour or two.

The army had been flung into the battle too. They had equivalent vehicles, but they were khaki. Canary-yellow armies and khaki armies were on manoeuvres everywhere, and having simply the time of their lives.

Writing about an event as grave and manifold as the great storm, it would be wrong to be frivolous. But it would be equally wrong to conceal the truth that for large numbers of people, the days that followed the storm were a really wonderful time. It shines through page after page of Bob Ogley's history, it shone through again and again among those I spoke to.

That this should have been so is no discredit to them, and no mockery of those who were full of grief at that time. The truth is that most of us are so constituted that we find few things in life more satisfying than to have a clear-cut job to do which brings immediate joy and relief to people in trouble, whom we meet face to face. It is all the more so when the job involves strenuous activity outdoors and when the end of the committment is clearly in sight.

Half the nostalgic invocations of the blitz spirit and of the dogged British character lean on an over-simplified recollection of the wartime crisis, when everything was subordinated to the one overwhelming imperative of survival. This time we were faced with a war where there need be no dreadful fears about not winning, or about the consequences of defeat. The knights-errant of the JCBs, however weary and harrassed they often were, were in an enviable situation, and in their hearts they knew it.

At times it sounds as if the rural south east was one immense adventure playground in those days, laced with a bracing strain of the surreal. A makeshift notice reading "Welcome to One Oak" was put up in Sevenoaks. Nuns were seen out in Hastings, hacking away at God's work with bow saws. Derek Wood, of Cuckfield, Sussex, was impressed to see a man from the electricity board struggling through the devastation on Friday morning, and amazed when he learned that he had only come to read the meter. At Standen, a National Trust property in Sussex, it took a team of 20 workers two days to hack their way down the drive. Before the drive was passable by car, a smart lady journalist came walking up it, and announced to the work-stained toilers: "I'm doing this article on Edwardian bedspreads . . ."

Christmas dinners were being eaten in Balcombe, Sussex, cooked on camping stoves, with whatever trimmings were available. They had been stored away in advance in deep freezes which were now starting to thaw. It became positively thrifty to stuff oneself with good things, before they went off. Even so, Mid-Sussex District Council alone collected five tons of doomed food from domestic freezers, and its inspectors condemned a similar amount stocked in food shops.

Friends invited to dinner to help empty the deep freeze would arrive bearing bottles to help the party go – not of wine, but of drinking water, suddenly precious in districts where the electric pumping stations had failed. Candles were improvised from old candle-ends, retrieved from the backs of drawers and melted down with old bootlaces for wicks.

Neighbours were thrown together forcibly by the emergency, perhaps after years of stand-offishly minding their own business on opposite sides of the garden fence. They made the best of their cold cookers and radiators by gathering for barbecues, sometimes sitting round the fire exchanging stories far into the night, before dispersing to their unheated bedrooms.

People found that they were very apt to burst into tears in the days after the storm, and a lot of weeping and comforting was going on, as well as much sharing and mucking in. "We had people sleeping on the floor in every room last night", Mrs Jeanette Woods told the *Ipswich Morning Star* the morning after the storm. The Red Cross in Ditchling, Sussex, was providing cooked lunches for up to 40 people a day in the village hall for most of the following week – free, but with a box to receive contributions.

Near Petworth, 77-year-old James Cooper Mitchell and his bedridden wife Audrey, who is 84, had to wait nine days for trees to be cleared from the track leading to their isolated cottage. Without electricity, he cooked over an open fire, and boiled water to keep his wife supplied with constant hot water bottles. Neighbours walked for miles across the fields to bring them supplies.

Local tree surgeons expressed indignation over rumours that dozens of tree surgeons from Scotland and the north were checking in at Sussex hotels and filching trade from under their noses at exorbitant rates. The police in Hastings warned the public that "cowboy" builders were abroad; one of them had asked £100 for replacing just three tiles. In some villages around Lewes it was reported that candles were changing hands at a pound a time, and the council urgently rustled up supplies of candles to meet the demand.

A young soldier fighting the good fight with his chain saw near Petersfield allegedly lopped the undergrowth so enthusiastically that he lopped off a wooden pole carrying power cables, and plunged several houses which had escaped harm in the storm into darkness.

I suspect that someone in East Anglia had been reading reports of the great New York power cut. The *Eastern Daily Press* ran a story after three days about fears of a local "baby boom", with the electricity board receiving urgent phone calls from husbands asking to be reconnected quickly – because, said one, candle-light dinners were making his wife "frisky". Why the cuts seem to have caused no such problems in Kent and Sussex, I cannot say.

The major rescue armies in the field were fighting under five banners. The local government force included works and social services employees in its ranks, as well as hastily-enlisted contractors (and even councillors, who were in the front line with the chainsaws in more than one village). The electricity boards put into the field an army with a peak strength of 5,000, including not only local workers, but also 2,000 others drafted in from other parts of the country – and 150 lent by the Irish Electricity Supply Board). British Rail had 400 people working on the lines in East Anglia alone over the weekend, with contractors from as far afield as Doncaster arriving to help. British Telecom threw in well over 1,000 workers from outside the area, and the armed forces themselves fielded about 1,000 more. Many of these workers were putting in 18-hour days in their determination to restore communications. In addition to these levies – not far short of 10,000 in all – was a motley but enthusiastic citizen army possibly as large again.

"There is a laid-down procedure for bringing us in – MACA, or Military Aid to the Civil Authority – a well-understood term in the circles", says Major David Innes, of the Royal School of Military Engineering, whose headquarters are in Aldershot. The students in its many local centres are aged between 20 and 35. "We operate at the invitation and in support of the county office. The army's role is restricted to situations where it is still deemed to be an emergency, not general clearing up. We had up to about 400 people assisting in the Kent area, operating in small teams, and we worked for two weeks.

"We have a lot of plant equipment, including cranes and diggers. We had limited training stocks of power saws and hand saws of various sizes, but we had to hire more – chain saws were a pretty premium item. We had four mobile generators in our area, and under the direction of the county council we sent them to provide electricity at places like old people's homes, and livestock premises: if I'd had six times the number of generators, I could have given them all out.

"As far as my personal work schedule is concerned, it was a disaster. As far as our students are concerned, they thought it was tremendous. In the ordinary way, plant operators would have been practising by shifting the same pile of earth from one end of a field to the other, and electricians would have been in the workshop wiring dummies. As it was they were out doing things to the National Grid. They thoroughly enjoyed it, and I must say, so did I."

All the repair workers were local heroes. "At the Fox and Hounds, the floor was sawdust, end to end – torches of every sort and flamboyant headgear all along the counters", wrote Hazel Pelling, landlady of a pub at Toys Hill, Sevenoaks, in one of the liveliest contributions to Bob Ogley's history of the storm. "Every hand that lifted a pint was grimed from manual exertion and from crawling through undergrowth. Every new arrival, commando-streaked and leaf-decorated, got a cheer. Mick Howard played 'If you go down in the woods today' and 'Whistle while you work'."

Deprived of piped water like many others, the Pellings put out buckets under the pub's leaking gutters and collected eight gallons in the torrential rain of the Friday night alone.

Bob Ogley himself, who is editor of the *Sevenoaks Chronicle*, was also deprived of electricity, but working away furiously all the while by candlelight at the text and pictures for *In the Wake of the Hurricane*. He finished the text in a week, and the book went on sale on November 30. National publishers had turned their noses up at it, so he created his own imprint, Froglets Press, achieving something close to next-day distribution with one delivery van and by packing up copies himself. Although it centres very much on the Sevenoaks area, the book touches on all the essentials and is full of first-hand material: we chroniclers of the storm all stand in debt to Ogley in much the same degree as all other epic poets stand in debt to Homer.

The battle to open up the wilderness was not without its real dangers. On the first morning, southern England was a snake-pit of live power cables, and it was only by good luck that nobody was killed by one. Tree-clearing has affinities with the game of spillikins; except that in this game, if the player releases the pent-up stresses in the heaped spills too carelessly, whole tree-trunks can spring into violent motion, and sweep him and his companions away.

The Royal Society for the Prevention of Accidents put out an urgent press notice two weeks after the storm, warning against the risks of using chain saws: "The storm inflicted enough destruction without making the aftermath a self-inflicted bloodbath", it said. There were already signs that inexpert users were hacking as much at themselves as at the fallen trees. The health authorities in Surrey and Sussex had been notified of seven serious chain saw injuries since the storm, in an area that would usually record two or three such injuries in a full year. Some rash spirits had been wielding chain saws while riding aloft in the bucket digger of a JCB, with unhappy results.

Even for experienced workers, the dangers were real. More than one of the armies had their casualties. A council worker near Tonbridge had been trapped by a fallen tree, and was taken to hospital with a suspected broken back. Geoffrey Stapleton, head gardener at Plumpton Place near Lewes, was killed by a falling branch while clearing the estate nearly a week after the storm. Gordon Marsh and Ian Rice, electricity workers from Lincolnshire and Merseyside, brought south to help reconnect the lines, died in the same way. So did Tony Telfer, a railway worker clearing debris near Gravesend.

There seems not to have been a single death, incidentally, among ordinary nitwits going out and breaking their necks scrambling through the undergrowth. Numbers of people in this category were in fact climbing over gates and slipping past "keep out" notices all over the place at this time. They must have showed a certain prudence as to what bowspring boughs they climbed on to, and what wooden swords of Damocles they strolled underneath, however. This is evidence of how effectively the publicity about the dangers had in fact gone home; and also speaks rather highly for ordinary nitwits.

Carving a way through the wilderness was stirring work, in spite of the risk, or just a little because of it. "There were men out everywhere in green anoraks, with axes over their shoulders having a whale of a time telling people which way to go, and generally taking charge of things", recalls Mrs Deborah Wearing. On the Sunday morning, she and her parents were among an expeditionary force of kith and kin of the McDonagh family, converging from three continents on the village of Edenbridge, in Kent.

The families of the two babies due to be christened at Edenbridge that morning had decided after consultations to go ahead as planned, since it would never be possible to covene the McDonagh international contingent again. The village had only just been restored to the map, and the route to it was almost buried in drifts of shrubbery.

"We started going to Edenbridge by all the sensible directions from London, and every road we went down we were turned back", says Mrs Wearing. "The men working on the roads practically had tears in their eyes with the excitement of it all. You could see them all feeling this great sense of comradeship, as if war had broken out and they were the Home Guard. At last we found we were coming towards the village practically from the south-east instead of north-west. There were broken trunks halfway across the road from both sides, and we had to zigzag from side to side to get by."

But about 70 people managed to find the way, though at least 20 more set out and vanished in the undergrowth. The McDonaghs are a large clan, with seven brothers and three sisters. They and their friends and relations had come from as far afield as Sydney, Wyoming and Newcastle-upon-Tyne to see Ben McDonagh and Thomas Kirkby (Mrs Wearing's nephew) duly and unforgettably baptised.

Behind its entanglements, the village was bright and sunny, with no sign of damage. The priest stood at the door after the service offering church candles – precious commodities now – to members of the congregation who were still without electricity.

Most major roads were clear in a day or two, but minor ones often had to wait much longer. Sevenoaks, effectively cut off on Friday morning, had most of its main roads clear by nightfall, but the A 25 east towards Maidstone, and the road south via Riverhill, remained closed for almost a week. So did the minor roads to Ide Hill, Westerham Hill and parts of Brasted Chart. As the roads were cleared, the power and telephone workers were able to move in.

Ordinary protocol often went overboard in the urgency of the job. "Bureaucracy's gone out of the window", Bruce Cova, chief executive for Sevenoaks District, told *The Observer*. Once the job of co-ordinating the local battle was in hand, he was out in the field with the troops. "We don't ask whose responsibility it is – if someone's got a tree through the roof and we've got a crane, we haul it out. We don't care if its a council house or private. The council tip closed at 5 pm and refused to take branches. I told him I'd drive a truck through his gates if he didn't open up. They call me John Wayne.

"I sent a man from the planning department across the fields in his shorts to see if the 30 people trapped in St Julian's Commune were dead or alive. He climbed out of a pile of wood and said: 'Hello: I'm from the District Council, are you all right ?' He was their first outside contact in three days. Maybe for the first time, people won't mind paying their rates. I hope they remember when they go up."

As the roads reopened, the relief workers found their efforts hampered by crowds of sightseers driving up to see the fun. The storm as spectacle is something we have not yet had to consider. But of course it was one of the great media events of the year. They had seen it on television, now they wanted to see it in the flesh. Already in the first sunny hours of Thursday, the photographers had been out in hordes on Sevenoaks cricket ground. Before long some residents were beginning to feel distinctly resentful towards the hordes of onlookers who made their misfortune a public event.

The subject was irresistible. Miles of film must have been shot off in the days that followed, as an expression of people's sense that they were witnessing an event of historic significance. The acres of devastation were subjects as tantalising as they were tempting for the camera, for once isolated on film there often proved to be curiously little difference between places which were amazing because they were suddenly clear of trees, and other places where there had never been any trees at all.

All the most enterprising local papers quickly saw that there was a market for pictures and stories, and brought out special supplements, the predominant tone of which was strangely festive. This was history before people's very eyes, overflowing with colour and human interest: there had been nothing to equal it since Prince Charles married Lady Di.

This natural curiosity – mixed with much goodwill, and readily tapped for contributions to replanting funds – also had its more thoughtless, darker side. In similar incidents in the past, sightseers have actually been a material obstruction to urgent life-saving measures. Matters never reached that point this time.

"Some people can be incredibly cruel", says Steve Thomas of the Robert de Mortain pub outside Hastings, where the storm brought down a chimney, as described in chapter seven. "Staff and friends were incredibly helpful. But some customers got quite annoyed when we had to tell them we couldn't supply a meal. And about three days after the storm, I saw three blokes standing at the side of the building, laughing over the damage. They weren't cheeky kids, they were men of 40 or 50. I went over to them and said: 'Would you mind buggering off? Three of us were nearly killed in there, and our livelihood was ruined. If you think that's funny, you can go and be sick somewhere else'.

"I don't think about what happened that much, but my wife hasn't really got over it yet. I think women tend to dwell on what might have been more than men do. It seems to have had little or no effect on Andrew. A couple of days after, he said 'Daddy . . . pub fell down', but that was about all."

On the Isle of Wight, sightseers arrived to admire the ruins of Shanklin Pier in such numbers that the whole town was filled with cars bumper to bumper all along the Esplanade. Spectators poured onto the beach in thousands, and scrambled over the twisted remains of the structure.

They were not all there just to look. Fred Sage, owner of the pier until the year before, commented to the local paper: "It really sickened me. What shocked me was the way some people moved in and began loading lorries and pick-up trucks. People were making off with whole trailer loads of timber and also fridges, tables and other gear."

Even the gates of the pier were lifted off their hinges and removed, after the padlock holding them had been forced.

All along the beach to the east of the pier, clearance workers had lit huge bonfires to dispose of the masses of timber washed away from the pier in its collapse. The flames lit up many animated figures sawing up the timber to take home as firewood. Lurid as the scene was, it is not illegal to appropriate flotsam in this way.

The age-old impulses of the wrecker were not reported on any scale except from the Isle of Wight. The cruellest refinement of the wrecker's art perhaps occurred at Blackgang, where Ken and Rita Smith had seen the massive pitched roof of their White Hotel bodily lifted from over their heads and hurled 150 feet, as described in chapter five. Thieves arrived almost before the wind had dropped, and stripped the roof of its lead sheathing.

As time went by, some people waiting for the restoration of electricity supplies began to crack under the strain. After three days, the number of electricity subscribers still without power had fallen to 400,000, but after that the pace of reconnection slowed down as repair workers began to grapple with more and more remote homesteads. Two weeks after the storm, electricity board workers working to restore power were met in some places with abuse and even assault. One was told he would be doused in petrol and set alight, another had the lights on his van shot out. A brick was thrown through the window of an electricity showroom in Crawley, Sussex, and a flare was thrown into another in Tunbridge Wells, fortunately without hurting anyone.

With the passing of the days, the disaster gradually underwent the customary transformation from shocking novelty to accustomed part of the nation's life. There were questions and debates in Parliament. Local and national politicians took up their positions on the storm question.

It was one of those awkward issues for a Conservative Government in which some of the party's own backbenchers were inclined to be vociferously plaintive on the victims' behalf – farmers, foresters, landowners with ruined shoots. The Opposition, meanwhile, were only too pleased to be plaintive too, on the principle that they would not have to milk the taxpayer of whatever funds were fixed on as appropriate Government aid.

It was plain from the first moment that there would have to be Government aid: the question was how much it should be. Landowners were faced with huge clearance and replanting costs. Conservation bodies would have to make safe and restore their ravaged amenities. Services like the NHS's hospitals had damage amounting to millions to repair on tight cash-limited budgets. Above all, local government had borne the brunt of the cost of emergency measures, and was faced in addition with large bills for repairing council buildings, homes and parks.

Grants of £3 million for amenity planting were made available through the Countryside Commission. A further £2 million was assigned for replacement of orchard trees. Historic gardens, the National Heritage fund, the royal parks and Kew Gardens were given £1,200,000 for restoration between them. An addition of £13.3 million was made to the NHS's budget. The overall total of Government assistance was £31 million, which the Government compared favourably with the £28 million which the French government had given out in aid.

But the big problem was local government. Being strongly committed to the principles of good housekeeping and self-sufficiency in local affairs, the Government was disposed not to mollycoddle the town halls. The sum of £18.3 million was made available, but only on strict conditions.

At this point I am afraid I shall have to talk about rate support grant. I do not much want to. Why should any reader be asked to consider the local rates when they are about to be swept away by a fully reformed system even more jerry-built and inequitable? But the details will affect the pockets of many in the storm-damaged areas, and might affect votes too. The main political questions about the storm are questions about local finance.

Briefly, the immediate public costs of the relief and restoration effort were in the main met by local government, the councils. The councils' two main sources of funds, in roughly equal amounts, are the rates – their own tax on property – and central government grants. To discourage councils from overspending, the government recently invented an ingenious system of penalties, so that if a council spends more than Whitehall thinks it should, its grant goes down.

Nicholas Ridley, the Secretary of State, announced the week after the storm that he would activate rules for natural disasters established after the severe winter of 1981–82. This meant that he would expect county councils to pay for as much of the damage as they could cover by raising the rates by a penny in the pound. Above this, the Government would pay out of general taxation for three-quarters of all further costs.

Consternation followed. The penalty system meant that any council already spending more than Whitehall said it ought would suffer an automatic loss of basic grant for everything it spent on the storm. The more it cost to clear up, the more the loss of basic grant would cancel out the special aid. Some councils like Kent, Norfolk and the Isle of Wight were in practice likely to lose more in penalties than they received in grants. Their ratepayers would be compelled to find practically the entire cost.

At first Mr Ridley insisted that this was what thrift was all about. Councils could not have foreseen the storm, but disasters of one kind or another were always cropping up, and they should have kept the equivalent of a penny rate up their sleeves to cover themselves.

In December he relented to the extent of allowing that councils would not have to pay penalties on their one-quarter share of spending above the penny rate. Their initial spending remained subject to penalties, but the change greatly softened the blow. In March, to draw the sting of a critical report from an all-party Commons committee, he also beefed up by £800,000 the grants available for the replanting of trees.

But it was estimated that the Government would still be taking back £9.8 million in penalties, so that its ostensible contribution to councils of £18.3 million would cost it only £8.5 million. A few councils, like Barnet, still seemed likely to lose more in penalties than they would gain in grant: Barnet's ratepayers would have to raise £170,000 to spend £100,000 on repairs. Many ratepayers who had almost forgotten the storm were due to get a nasty surprise when next year's rate demand came in.

Some other loose ends could be tidied up here in passing. The unhappy Met Office spent the months that followed the storm forecasting appalling weather so as to avoid all risk of being caught out again. The winter proved to be an exceptionally mild one, however. In February, the Met Office took delivery of its new computer, a £5 million job with an effective capacity eight times that of the old one.

Lord Marshall ordered the production of a promotional video, trumpeting the victories of the Central Electricity Generating Board in the crisis. They proved hard to unload: three were sent to the *New Scientist*, and at least three more found their way to *The Times*. But the Government had set its heart on dismemberment of the CEGB, and in February its doom was announced.

In spite of the biggest payout in their history after a single disaster, the big insurance companies ended the financial year with profits well above average. This did not stop them from citing the storm as a reason for raising their premiums sharply. But to do them justice, I found few of their customers seriously dissatisfied with the way they had risen to the occasion.

Marjorie Doddington, whose roof flew away in chapter seven, finally saw her daughter married in January. She had saved the sausage rolls and prawns in her deep freeze all this time, and took them across to Dorking for the reception.

The statues of Antony Gormley were in the wars again a few weeks after the storm. A figure with arms outstretched like a crucifixion, which stood on the walls of Londonderry, in Northern Ireland, was defaced with the stigmata of sectarian graffiti.

Lord Brockway died in April, six months short of his one hundredth birthday. His broken statue, its arms snapped off, had spent many months in the ladies' toilet at the Conway Hall in Red Lion Square. An appeal to pay for the repair of the statue moved only slowly towards the £4,000 that the sculptor, Ian Walters, was asking. When Geoffrey Austin, the manager of the hall, made his rounds before locking up, he would sometimes be caught off his guard, and would give the statue a nervous 'hello'.

Roy Couzens, acting coxwain of the Dover lifeboat, recovered from his heart attack, but had to retire from the lifeboat service on health grounds. The Royal National Lifeboat Institution awarded him its silver medal for bravery, and gave bronze medals to the six other members of the crew. The Weymouth coxwain, Derek Sargent, earned a bronze medal, too, for his night's vexations.

The European Commission sent £5,000 to the relatives of each of the 25 who died in the storms out of its special disaster fund. The British Government, which had not made a similar gesture, made no public expression of gratitude. Hosts of goodwill saplings were dispatched to Britain by friendly nations, twin cities and concerned individuals, to help with replanting.

Bob Ogley's history of the storm sold 30,000 copies, raised over £10,000 for the local tree-planting appeal, and went into a second edition part of whose profits were to be donated to the National Trust's disaster appeal. A copy of the book was buried in a time-capsule under the roots of one of the seven oak saplings planted at Sevenoaks, perhaps to rise to the daylight again three hundred years hence, when the next hurricane comes.

Off the Spanish coast, the *Herald of Free Enterprise* was brought under tow again, after five days adrift. But with a will to live worthy of a less ill-starred vessel, the ferry made another bid for liberty off the Cape of Good Hope in December. The ghosts on board saw in the New Year while wallowing adrift once more in the gales of the Roaring Forties. It was not until the end of March that the ship entered harbour for the last time among the shipbreaking yards of Taiwan.

"Our dear old *Hengist*" was refloated a week after the storm, and went back into service in January, after a refit.

I hesitated rather apprehensively before seeking to tie up one of the story's loose ends, because I half expected to hear sad news. I suspected that the Home Office might not have loosed its grasp so easily on the Tamil detainees so surprisingly snatched to freedom from the ferry *Earl William* in chapter fifteen. Perhaps they had been quietly removed to other places of detention, or even sent back to Sri Lanka, where the political situation was a little quieter than it had been. But six months after the storm, I found Mr Maharasingam still in buoyant spirits. They had not been given permission to stay, but they had been allowed to live where they wished. Most had been found jobs in businesses run by the Tamil community; one was studying at college.

It seemed possible that the ill wind really had blown lasting good fortune their way. But the Home Office commented: "Their cases will be resolved. Temporary admission isn't time-barred, and it's not a formal acceptance of entry into the United Kingdom. Very few cases take years to resolve, mercifully, but it can take many months." It is early days yet.

The wait for power to be restored was a long one for some. At the peak during the morning of the storm, the power cuts had affected about 4 million consumers. Most of them were reconnected by mid-morning on October 16. By October 21, the number of households without supply was still 168,000. A week later, some 25,000 were still without supply. By now East Anglia was largely reconnected, and power workers from there had been shifted south. By October 29, 4,000 homes were still waiting to be reconnected, and virtually all of these had power again by the end of the month.

A minority had to wait far longer for telephones than for power. After a week, all except 80,000 subscribers had been reconnected. But by November 20, more than a month after the storm, there were still 3,000 awkward cases waiting for their lines to be restored: some of them had to wait several weeks longer still.

The experience of those weeks without electricity was among the strangest of the consequences of the storm. A curious stillness fell. For all the vexations of life without power, many of those who endured that time, in isolated hamlets, recall it as something that they remember with more pleasure than pain. The strange isolation of rural Kent, only 25 or 30 miles from central London, was never so eerily intense as it was now. In the village of Goathurst Common, the power lines were not restored for 13 days. Down the hill in the evenings, the villagers were able to gaze through swathes newly torn through the surrounding woods, down to the tantalisingly close, yet inaccessibly remote, lights of Tunbridge Wells.

"It is something that I would not have missed", says Jane Iles, who lives in the village with her husband Falcon and four children, ranging in age at the time from seven months to sixteen years. "Everything took much longer. We had no hot water, because our solid fuel heating doesn't work unless the electric pump is going. I had to start cooking the evening meal on our wood burning stove at about two in the afternoon, because it had to be ready so that we could eat it before it got dark.

"In the evenings we used to huddle in one room around the stove. We got on each others' nerves in the evening. The children couldn't go off to their rooms, and they got bored and wanted the TV. We played lots of card games and Trivial Pursuit. They were overwhelmed with joy when the TV came on again.

"But it was so nice in some ways. We talked so much more to neighbours. You had to: and what one person didn't have, you shared.

"At the beginning, we didn't think it was going to last, and so we lit candles all over the house, But then we began to realise it might take a long time, and we cut down. Of course, you couldn't buy candles or torch batteries anywhere by then. We did run out, but we had several offers from people who helped us out.

"We were snowed up for a week the winter before, so we have got used to adapting to circumstances. The children's first reaction was to be pleased – we put the battery radio on and it said the schools were closed – it was a bit of an adventure. My eldest daughter was worried, because she was doing her A-level course, and she had no evenings to do her homework. But they all learned to do it as soon as they got in from school while the daylight lasted. They still talk about our time without power quite a lot.

"There was just a deathly hush for days, until they opened the road up. After that we were able to drive out to the shops and to school.

"When the power came back on, I had to readjust all over again. We had just adjusted to the old days, where you had to get on with what needed doing, and it took a long time. Then all of a sudden you had so many choices to make – shall I Hoover or shall I iron? It was strange".

The games of Trivial Pursuit or Scrabble by the light of oil-lamps became one of the motifs of the aftermath. The rebirth of family life round the hearth was a popular cliche, but more than a cliche for many of those who experienced it.

"We have slipped back to the landscape of 80 or more years ago, and a lifestyle to match", Hazel Pelling of the Fox and Hounds pub wrote in her diary. "Candlepower and water collection, communication by personal visit or letter, rural timbering pursuits, house mending and patching, walks and early nights. 'Your father and I played Patience last night', said Eileen to their astonished daughter Alicia. 'I think you and father have made more conversation during these three days than you have in a year', said Alicia".

At the same time as people in rural Norfolk, Kent, Sussex and the Isle of Wight were discovering the compensations of a life of nineteenth-century self-sufficiency, the story was entering the same phase far away in Brittany.

Le Monde, now fully awakened to the picturesque possibilities of the theme, waxed nostalgic about *"Les veillées des chaumières bretonnes"* "Vigils in the cottages of Brittany".

On opposite sides of the Channel the same elements recurred – the family gathered around the communal meal prepared with antique labour, eating in "the flickering yellow halo of a paraffin lamp"; the perpetual fire glowing in the hearth; the closer links between old and young, gathered round the fire; the surprising discovery that life was possible without television; the claim "We have never talked together like this before . . .".

"When the lights came on again in our village", one young Breton farmer is quoted as saying, "we all came out onto the road, shouting and laughing like mad things". So it was in many a village in England too. But the joy was not entirely unmixed with regret. As the electricity board's workers closed in on the last few households still without power, a spokesman said that they had had a number of requests to be the very last house to be switched on.

CHAPTER 19

NESTS FOR THE HERON

"The storm has gone over me; and I lie like one of those old oaks which the late hurricane has scattered about me. I am stripped of my honours; I am torn up by the roots, and lie prostrate on the earth."
(Edmund Burke: *A Letter to a Noble Lord,* 1796)

Exotic visitants appeared in the dishevelled gardens of two houses in Brentford and Isleworth in the days after the wind dropped. Owners inspecting the damage caught sight of glimmers of iridescent blue among the litter, and discovered tropical butterflies lurking there in a daze – two Brazilian Owls, blue with owl-eye markings on their undersides.

They were fugitives from the smashed Butterfly House at Syon, tumbled through the woods for distances of up to a mile and a half, and yet somehow unscathed. The temperatures they would have been used to in their native rain-forests would be up to 85° (30° Celsius). In the unnatural warmth of the night, the temperature had risen as high as 63° (17° Celsius), but it had fallen about 18° (10°) by morning, and the insects would soon have fallen into a stupor. One had found refuge in a potting shed. It was brought back alive after five days and made a full recovery. The other was returned nine days after the storm, still alive but so weak that it could not be saved. Both must have found scraps of rotten fruit to eat, to have lasted so long.

The image of escaped butterflies so caught the public imagination that more than 200 people called the centre to announce that they had found one of its fugitives, and many of them brought their finds in. It does not say much for British awareness of natural history that all of these except the two Owls proved to be homely Red Admirals and Commas, roused out of hibernation. The centre gave them house-room in its domestic butterfly section.

Perhaps it is not as incongruous as it seems that they came safely through weather which had levelled church spires and overturned articulated lorries. The tropics have storms of their own, and natural selection must have bred tactics for survival into the most fragile looking specimens. The sturdy American Monarch butterfly regularly makes migrations of hundreds of miles, bucking against the prevailing wind and taking shelter if it becomes unduly strong: several individuals have turned up in Britain after having fluttered clean across the Atlantic.

We know that at Great Yarmouth, a mere flick of a wing away from the weather station at Gorleston, the wind must have reached velocities of about 120 mph. Yet here too, on the very edge of the North Sea, people with shops and homes along the seafront turned up at the shattered Yarmouth Butterfly Centre for days afterwards, bringing back ten or fifteen precious insects, some from distances of more than a mile away.

Howlett's Zoo got its clouded leopards back before they ate anybody. They were lingering near their enclosure next day, but one, a male called Xiang, made off when he saw people around.

The *Daily Telegraph*, an indispensable if slightly owlish source for news of the aftermath of the storm, reported on the following Tuesday that he had been spotted in the woods, but was still at large. Spike Milligan, himself a victim of the storm and "homeless under a Sussex tree", wrote gaily next day to say that it was unnecessary to report that a leopard had been spotted, since leopards were always spotted.

"We put a trap out, and tempted it back with meat after just a week", says Robert Boutwood, the manager. "He'd probably been living on dead birds – there were lots of them all over, crows and so on – crushed or disorientated, I suppose."

Posses of keepers went out to round up Howletts' escaped Capuchin monkeys in nearby gardens: none had got more than a mile away.

Mr Boutwood's evidence of heavy casualties among wild birds is striking, but seems to have been exceptional. Nick Marx noticed nothing unusual of the kind. "During the summer a magpie had a go at a greenfinches' nest, and someone brought me the only surviving fledgling. I raised him and ultimately let him go, but he kept coming back. On the day of the storm, I was concerned it might have killed him, but he reappeared on the Friday, so he was still alive then. But I've never seen him since."

Many observers agree, however, that the behaviour of birds changed markedly for some days after the storm. They seemed to have disappeared at first; when they were seen again, they were oddly quiet and shy. It seemed to me in London that the broken woods were tempting many down to low levels at which they felt insecure; but the effect will have varied from species to species.

Ornithologists and wildlife researchers were not plunged into quite the same deep gloom into which foresters were thrown by the storm. Detailed monitoring of its effects on wildlife will take months, but initial findings suggest that it may have done more good than harm in this area, with some exceptions.

"When you look at the scale of the devastation, it's difficult to see how thrushes, finches and birds like that could actually have coped", says Dr Rob Fuller, of the British Trust for Ornithology. "The bodies of birds like that would be most unlikely to be found, in the state the woods were in. My guess is that the effect will have varied very much from place to place.

"The main thing is the distinction between immediate casualties and long-term changes in habitats. Wild populations are usually able to recover from events like a cold winter which cause many deaths. But we know very little about how birds react to changes in habitat.

"You're dealing with an almost unique event, for which no case-studies exist. We want to treat this as an opportunity to see how birds react to a major change of this kind – it's quite exciting.

"But some species should actually be better off – woodpeckers, nuthatches and other birds living off insect life in decaying timber, for instance. Where the forest canopy has been opened up, the variety of plants, birds and animals may be enriched. But a bird like the rook, or the heron, which keeps coming back to large, permanent nests in trees, is going to find a lot of them have gone."

This was a particular point of anxiety in the ravaged bird sanctuaries of East Anglia. The heronries at Orford and Rendlesham Forest suffered severely. Naturalists in those districts were also anxious about the red squirrel, one of the few mammals which was expected to be seriously threatened by the impact of the storm on habitats. Over most of Britain, the red squirrel has been displaced by the more robust grey: whatever special factors had enabled it to hang on in a corner of Suffolk might have been disrupted by such drastic changes in the landscape.

But most small mammals living in the woods would be likely to find a glut of food brought down from above to help them through the winter. It is customarily tidied up in managed woodlands, but this year there would be ample supplies.

Tree pipits, warblers and similar birds find the early stages of young woodland a congenial habitat. So do woodland butterflies like the fritillaries. Plants like anemones and violets also take advantage of an opening in the woodland roof, and more than one naturalist predicted that 1988 would prove to be a vintage primrose and bluebell year, and 1989 better still, as the flowers spread into new niches. For the most part, naturalists reacted to the catastrophe with barely suppressed glee. "It is one of the most interesting things to have happened in my time as an ecologist", says Dr George Peterken of the Nature Conservancy Council. "The effects on wildlife must in general be beneficial. It increases the variety of woodland, and that creates new habitats.

"I'd like owners to look out for opportunities for natural restocking – to delay replanting four or five years and see if the saplings already there can't take over."

There was special concern for lichens, however. "Some lichens are very poor colonisers, and tend to spread only by vegetative means", says Tony Whitbread of the N.C.C. "We shall be taking samples of the bark with rare colonies and literally gluing them to living trees. The oak is the most important tree for lichens, and in the natural course of events it can take 50 or even 100 years to rot down. That gives lichens time to transfer to younger trees as they grow up.

"But modern forest management doesn't favour that. We have a worry that more damage may be caused by people tidying up than by the storm itself. The message is getting across to owners and managers, but it is easy to feel guilty if you don't tidy up."

One of the Nature Conservancy Council's first acts after the storm was to hurry out to Windsor Forest to check on the fate of a single dead tree. Britain's most endangered insect, the violet click beetle *Limoniscus violaceus* is only known to survive in this one tree, and perhaps in other rotting stumps round about. Happily the cadaver was still standing.

Commercial researchers from a Slough "bio-technology boutique" were almost as quick to descend on Burnham Beeches, in Berkshire, to study the array of exposed roots of trees struck down there. They were looking for colonies of bacteria, which can survive undisturbed for hundreds of years among trees' roots, and have sometimes evolved elaborate chemical defences against their environmental competitors.

Like the many expeditions sent in haste to explore the microbiological secrets of the tropical rain forests before they are mown down and destroyed, the researchers were scrabbling among the roots in search of natural microbes which might be of medical value. Their primary goals were chemicals that control tumour growth and anti-inflammatory agents which might inhibit the breakdown of tissue in rheumatoid arthritis.

As for Lord Massereene and Ferrard's herons, they did return on St Valentine's Day. They disdained the platform he had put up for them, but nested in other trees not far off, though with some signs of discomfort at not being able to lodge in the amiable proximity that they used to enjoy.

For the kind of bird-watcher teasingly called a "twitcher", the storm was a bonanza of a memorable kind. Toothsome rarities to be seen included the yellow-billed cuckoo (reported in Lincolnshire), the North American veery (which had the twitchers jostling on Lundy Island), the Pallas warbler, (which usually migrates between Siberia and east Asia, and was identified in Suffolk), Leach's petrel (Datchet reservoir) and the predatory Arctic skua (marauding on exhausted gulls on several London reservoirs). It is not surprising that birds from the north as well as the south were observed: it was a south wind which blew our trees down, but the wind on the depression's western side blew almost as strongly from the north.

"We have seen a very large number of Sabine's gulls", says Dr Fuller. "It is quite unprecedented – 150 to 200 turned up inland, in groups in some cases. They stayed a few days, fed themselves up, and set out again to the south. They should have no problems finding their way back to their wintering grounds. A Manx shearwater was once recorded to have flown from Wales to South America – a much greater distance – in just 12 days. Sabine's gull is a very beautiful bird, comparable to a black-headed gull. I'd seen the odd one flashing past in stormy weather, but nothing like this before".

One could fill a book with stories about animals from the storm. In Maldon, Essex, contractors repairing storm damage at the Blue Boar Hotel were put to flight by a swarm of bees disturbed by the weather (the old rhyme does not say what a swarm of bees is worth in October: perhaps because not much rhymes with October). In Bexhill a sulphur-crested cockatiel was found in the wreckage of a tree and subsequently re-housed under the name of Hurricane. A goose called Archie was buried under garden debris for nine days in Bexhill, before being discovered alive but hungry. Mrs Peggy Ward of Attleborough, Norfolk, announced in the *Eastern Daily Press* that she was launching a parrot rescue service, to reunite storm-bound parrots with their owners. Miss Heather Humby's four Siamese cats in the Isle of Wight all found their way back to her in the morning: but then they did have 36 lives between them.

For farmers, the storm raised problems which had nothing comic about them. As in France and the Channel Islands, the power cuts faced them with threatening difficulties. Electric generators were as precious in Sussex and Hampshire as they were in Brittany. Peter Barton, owner of three poultry farms near Haywards Heath, protested four days after the storm that the army had a stock of generators and was refusing to let local farmers use them. He had 100,000 birds which were dead or dying because they were in darkness and could not see to eat. Mr Roger Stiles, a dairy farmer near Godalming, claimed that he was having to throw away 2,500 litres of milk a day because he could not cool it.

Graeme and Pearl Callaway on the Isle of Wight were almost at the point of calling in a vet to slaughter their herd of 150 cows when neighbours stepped in to rescue them. "The cows had recently calved and they were heavy with milk, but without electricity we couldn't milk them", Mrs Callaway told the local paper. The cows were in such pain that it seemed that they would be obliged to put them out of their misery. "We tried to hire a generator, but none was available – other farmers had the same problem". On Saturday, when they were about to call the vet, two local farmers provided generators for them. But the delay in milking had caused mastitis in some of the cows, and put others off milking for a time.

Fruit and vegetable growers found when they sought to replace their glasshouses that the cost of doing so had risen threefold since the night of the storm, and remained high even though suppliers from all over Europe were bidding for the work. Soft fruit growers were aggrieved that the Government proposed to pay orchard growers £2 for every tree they had lost, while strawberries, gooseberries, vines and hops attracted no such relief.

The National Farmers' Union estimated in January that its own insurance society had handled claims on damage to buildings and livestock amounting to more than £24 million, but stressed that this represented only a fraction of total costs, which it estimated must run into hundreds of millions. The Country Landowners Association claimed that the £2,750,000 which the Government had allocated for distribution by the Countryside Commission had been three times over-subscribed and would in the main go to local authorities and not to private landowners; it pointed out with some acerbity that those countryside stalwarts, the London boroughs, had bid for £2,500,000 of this by themselves. The Government's response was "piecemeal and meagre", it said.

But it was from the forestry industry that the most dramatic statistics of devastation came. It took months before serious assessments of the scale of the disaster began to emerge. Estimates had gradually floated up from a million trees to five million and even ten. But the authoritative report of the specially-appointed Forest Windblow Action Committee announced in January that "at least 15 million trees" had been blown down.

The volume of timber in these trees was nearly four million cubic metres. If it was gathered together in a single cube, sandpapered and burnished up with a coat of french polish, it would stand as high, wide and deep as a twelve-storey building, but solid through and through.

Over entire counties, around 20 per cent of woodland stock had been lost, and the proportion of broad-leaved woodland, as distinct from conifers, was unprecedentedly high – roughly half. More than two-thirds of the lost timber was on private estates. Some timbers, like oak, can lie on the ground for several years without deteriorating. Others – beech in particular – discolour fast. Much of it would have to be harvested within the year if it was to be of any commercial value. The volume of timber involved was about two-thirds of the total volume used by the British timber industry in a year; but a high proportion of it was hardwood, for which there were limited specialist markets: much was too old for use, or too much damaged in its fall.

Timber is so bulky that it is normally uneconomic to transport it far outside the immediate area. The fallen timber represents five years' normal local output and there is certain to be a glut there for years to come. Sawmill prices for softwood pulp dropped by half immediately after the storm. To mitigate this problem, the Windblow report recommended a special 15-month subsidy of £2,500,000 to help owners transport timber away to other parts of Britain, and £4 million over five years to encourage replanting.

It calculated that the cost merely of clearing useless timber before replanting would range between £500 and £1,500 per hectare, with broadleaves costing the most. Replanting would cost up to £500 per hectare for conifers and up to £1,000 for broad-leaved woodlands. Grants are available for replanting, but the special chaos left by the storm was such that many owners were daunted by the labour of months or even years that would be needed even to reach the point where that would be possible, where less accessible woodland was concerned. Many were half-complaining, half-threatening, that they would be forced to leave their plantations as rotting wildernesses more or less permanently – a threat which had no terrors for naturalists, at least. The action committee's report agreed that these costs would be significantly higher than usual.

Britain's compensation fund for foresters amounted to £1 million: in France, for a timber loss which was almost double, the compensation was fifteen times as great.

The Government took a wary view of the Windblow Action Committee's proposals, and one distressed landowner was told by a former minister that the Secretary of State was right not to "spend taxpayers' money to help you rebuild your shoot." No official yes or no was given to the proposal for a transport grant, either when the committee reported or at the Commons debate in March. As the months went by, the tons of beech wood lying out in the winter rain gradually began to deteriorate.

Proposals were made to snatch some benefit from the disaster by using some of the rare types of timber suddenly made available to produce fine works of craftsmanship. These would serve as some mitigation of the loss, and as a kind of memorial. The craftsman joiner John Makepeace was in the forefront of these moves. Several large-scale furniture makers, including Habitat and Ercol, considered launching special brands labelled "Saved from the Storm", to help put to use trees which would otherwise be left to rot. "We have been trying to create a fashion for beech for years", a Habitat director said.

In fact, nothing came of this project, which later became a source of mild embarrassment to the manufacturers. It involved a high risk of ending up with furniture at prices the consumer would reject, or else of appearing to profit out of a national disaster.

"We would have loved to help, but it was impossible", says Tony Brown of Ercol. "We have to keep up our standards. We select our timber while it is standing, and it is felled carefully. The fallen timber was all sizes, and you couldn't tell by looking at it what sort of shakes and flaws it had inside after the stresses it had been through. The quantity of usable stuff was really quite small".

Meanwhile at least one cargo of 1,500 tons of beech from the National Trust's Slindon estate, near Arundel, was shipped to Turkey, 3,000 miles away, where the furniture trade is better equipped to digest small shipments. The resulting chairs and tables were unlikely ever to be stamped "Saved from the Storm."

John Makepeace believes that our own industry is not flexible enough to take advantage of an opportunity of this kind: "It is true that much of the fallen wood was damaged or inaccessible. But in any case, the import trade in hardwoods is so strong, with its lines of supply so well-established, that the domestic producer finds it hard to compete. There is no incentive to try, so the trade dwindles.

"We are enormously wasteful of timber in this country. No attempt is made to find a use for the smaller thinnings, which brought a significant proportion of the profits in the past. The storm has left a deep scar on owners who have had heavy losses, and may not want to risk planting again.

"Those stories about a bonanza of rare wood for the craftsman were a myth. At Kew, there is a plan to build a display cabinet for the Sir Joseph Banks building out of wood from a casualty of the storm – probably a black walnut tree which many people have fond memories of, because it was in an especially prominent position. They mean to do the same kind of thing at the Chelsea Physic Garden. The cabinets will be worthwhile memorials, and useful too. But I can go down to the East End and buy any amount of imported black walnut any time, quite cheaply."

Like those economic forces which dictate that it is preferable to tow an unwanted ship to shipbreakers on the other side of the world, instead of dismantling it where it lies, the economics of the timber trade dictate that a cabinet maker in Sussex may find it cheaper to use timber from a tree felled in Brazil, instead of one blown down in his garden . . . while the latter may find a ready buyer in Ismir or Bodrum.

The Windblow Committee's figures set out the context in which immediate decisions about clearing and replanting would be made. But in the longer term, new factors are likely to be fed into the economic equation.

By historical chance, the storm came at a time which is likely to be a turning point in the story of forestry in Britain. It is becoming apparent even to politicians that the basis of funding for European agriculture is ceasing to be tenable. The regular set-piece confrontations at Brussels or Strasbourg over EEC budgets are largely diversionary procedures, designed to avoid grappling seriously with the fact that the Community cannot indefinitely organise its pricing system so as to encourage rising production of produce that is not needed. Brittany and East Anglia are examples of an artificial agricultural boom which can no more go on upwards for ever than the Stock Exchange's bull market could have done.

Agricultural productivity will have to be made less attractive (for instance by taxing fertilisers, with all the pollution problems they cause) or by giving greater inducements to farmers to manage land for amenity as well as for output. In the south-east, unwanted farmland will be vulnerable to development pressures. Returning land to woodland will be one of the ways Europe will find to solve its problem.

In this country, the storm jolted us into a sharper appreciation of the truth that trees do not just happen, in a managed landscape like our own. Without wise policies of planting and care, the countryside would grow threadbare, and would in particular be emptied of those broad-leaved trees whose presence is splendid but whose return on investment is minimal. Subsidy or the lack of subsidy is already the major influence in shaping the industry.

If the storm's impact on our awareness is durable, it could set the context in which these issues will be debated in the years ahead.

A landscape formed by policies designed to restrain agricultural overproduction might look foreign to our eyes today. The familiar pattern of field and hedgerow might be replaced by a pattern more broadly massed, with large fields, fewer hedgerows and more extensive clumps of woodland on less fertile ground.

It would be foolish to feel unduly dejected at this prospect. The English landscape has changed many times in history, from the communal strip-farming of the Saxons and the enclosures of the 18th century, to the ravages in our own day of Dutch Elm Disease (which killed fewer trees in ten years than the storm killed in a night), and the rise and decline of oil-seed rape – a momentary dazzling yellow flash in our rural history, switched on by subsidy and perhaps soon to be switched off again by subsidy. If John Constable could see Dedham Vale today, he would have to be a philosopher not to weep.

Dr Oliver Rackham warns us against the "Kaleidoscope Myth" in his magisterial *History of the English Landscape*, which has set on a basis of evidence so much that was previously based on legend and guesswork. He shows that despite all changes, many features of the landscape have proved extraordinarily durable – and even some living individuals, like the giant "stools" of coppiced ash, which may be as much as 1,000 years old. He is scornful of modern wholesale forestry, and of "the blight of tidiness which every year sweeps away something of beauty or meaning".

"Much of England in 1945 would have been instantly recognisable by Sir Thomas More, and some areas would have been recognised by the Emperor Claudius", he says in the book. But after the war, "as much ancient woodland was destroyed in 25 years as in the previous 400 years."

The changes that now face us imply no such wholesale threat. If the new woods are planned so as not to encroach on areas rich in wildlife, like chalk downland or Fenlands, they need not impair what remains, and can even enhance it.

Ancient woodland is relatively resistant to storm damage, if it is given time to regenerate. Outside rich men's parks, the most enduring mark of the storm on the landscape may be on hedgerow trees.

To our eyes, the pattern of hedgerows is an essential element in the beauty of what we think of as the English scene. But the great John Ruskin used to rail at the hedgerow as inherently unaesthetic: "Perhaps nothing in the whole compass of landscape is so utterly unpicturesque and unmanageable [to the artist] as the ordinary English patchwork of field and hedge, with trees dotted over it in independent spots".

It is just those trees "dotted . . . in independent spots", which appeal to us so much, and are especially threatened today. They are left-overs of a system which has been growing moribund for some time. The hand-tended hedge has had little place in progressive farming practice since the war, and many single trees which had originally been encouraged to spring from the hedgerow were left alone in the middle of fields after a grant had been earned by grubbing up the hedge. They are relics of a lost pattern, and whether they went down on the night of the storm, or survived trailing a wake of broken branches far to leeward, it will be difficult to devise or justify realistic incentives for replacing them.

Ruskin would be pleased to see the country reverting more closely to the condition of a painting by Claude Lorrain. Our own feelings are necessarily more mixed. The eye grows used to the pattern of its day, and attached to it, because it reveres something which lies deeper than superficial patterns. What is certain is that our descendants – barring some gross breach of trust with our heritage – will find the landscape they are used to appropriate and natural, and might find our own faintly alien. It is a troubling thought as well as a comforting one that those who do not remember southern England as it was before October 16, 1987, will not even miss it.

CHAPTER 20

RUINED CASTLES

"Vix ea nostra voco" ("I scarcely call these things our own")
Hussey family motto, Scotney Castle

"When I got up the next morning and found that the drive was completely buried in trees, so that you couldn't even see where it went – I literally packed up", says Mick Martin, head gardener at Scotney Castle, a National Trust property 40 miles east of Petworth and 15 miles south of Knole. "We didn't have the will power at first even to make a start. The logistics of it were too much even to think about.

"Absolute despair – that was the first sensation. I kept feeling that I must be going to wake up at any moment."

The half-dozen ground staff of the castle sent an expedition across the fields to see how the marooned staff of the house had fared (it was nearly a week before communication by car and telephone was restored). Before they could set about the overwhelming task of clearance, the emergency services commandeered them and their equipment for the essential service of helping to clear the main local roads.

It was not until the next day that a serious start could be made on excavating a way to the house, and plunging into the garden as if it was a tropical forest, to begin to assess the damage. Mr Martin had been at Scotney for 14 years, and the experience of seeing his efforts and plans of so many years turned to a mockery, as well as the achievements he had inherited, must have been a deeply shocking one. He was able to throw himself into the task of reconstruction within hours, and there was so much to do that there was little time left over for lamentations.

But at some National Trust properties staff suffered a more enduring collapse of morale, and the Trust had to devote considerable time and patience in the weeks that followed to persuading them that the effort really was worth while. Nobody who saw the overthrown limbs on the ground, the lawns heaved up by snapped roots as if by subterranean explosions, and the trees which had survived as scarred and crooked poles, with their branches bodily torn away, would find such problems surprising.

Many workers, after all, were not able to turn their backs on the destruction at the end of the day. Their homes were in the midst of it. "Its like living in Passchendaele or the Somme", said one, and the resemblance was real enough.

Scotney was a major loss. Its main character was set in a later age than Knole and Petworth, and its spirit was altogether more romantic and less charged with public purpose. The castle that gives it its name is a diminutive atom of defiance built in the 1370s, when the French were making armed raids into Kent. Set in a rather stagnant moat, it was the kind of irregular, cramped and aguey dwelling that squires great and small were knocking down all through the 17th and 18th centuries, as·they moved into more comfortable quarters.

This example of the type survived long enough to start looking interesting again. In the 1830s the Hussey family moved uphill to a new castle built of stone quarried from the hill itself. (In the quarry can be seen fossilised footprints of iguanodon dinosaurs, which browsed off the gingko-tops beside the Wealden Sea before such a thing as an oak tree or a lime existed: though when the petrified footprints were made, the storm-resistant fossil tree at the Natural History Museum had already been a fossil longer than they have been yet).

But instead of demolishing the half-ruinous old castle, Edward Hussey saw its potential as the centrepiece of a garden. He devised one which looked back to the landscape tradition of William Kent, Capability Brown and Humphry Repton, and also forward to the "pictorial naturalism" of Gertrude Jekyll and her contemporaries at the end of the century. It was one of the most significant progenitors of a host of domestic gardens throughout Britain.

He artfully assisted the picturesque dilapidations of the castle, made sure that the quarry was opened at a spot where it too could be exploited for dramatic effect, and organised the planting so as to reveal ingeniously varied views, high, low, widespread and intimate. A number of fine mature trees were already growing there. Shelter belts of firs were planted to make a mild climate milder, so that it could support the wealth of shrubs and flowers which he selected, contriving to keep the ruin half-buried almost throughout the year in roses, buddleia, phlox, liquid-ambar or rhus.

In the storm the garden lost 183 of its 531 trees, including a princely cedar of Lebanon, 12 out of its 23 oaks, 19 out of its 58 yews, and 8 out of its 13 limes. The largest lime, struck down on the main lawn beside the moat, was the oldest of its kind in Britain – a tree 293 years old, with a height of 111 feet and a girth of 19 feet. Another lime, eight years its junior, slimmer but ten feet higher, came down too. The garden lost its oldest oak, its oldest yew and a 171-year-old specimen of the chequer tree, or sorbus, or wild service – a tree common in ancient woodland, but now quite rare. It, too, was regarded as the biggest of its kind left in Britain.

Less venerable and conspicuous, but at least as significant to the fate of the garden, were the sheltering ranks of sequoias – the "tall tree garden" – and Monterey pines, which had helped to create the conditions in which its azaleas, ferns and rhododendrons could flourish. Many rare species had already been crushed by the falling of the trees. It was impossible to speculate how many would fail to adapt to the new colder climate.

Smaller trees borne down in the fall of the great ones included some which had been planted as their eventual heirs. Christopher Hussey, the last private owner of the castle, had spent years planning its future, so that as trees reached the end of their natural lives their successors would be ready and waiting. The unnatural sport of nature which overtook his plans promoted some understudies to starring roles before their time, and wiped out others at the moment their chance should have come.

In their fall, the great trees ripped patches many yards wide out of the smooth lawns. The torn and crumpled turf, hanging in frayed strips from the edges of the upturned slabs of soil, resembled the baize of a billiard table attacked by a maniac. In places the effect was of entire little lawns growing eccentrically on edge. One cedar had stood beside a timber fence, and in falling it lifted turf and fence together, so that the split-wood rails continued in a lunatic curve until the fence was completely on its side eight feet above the ground, a barrier to keep out angels, before it curved down to resume its more prosaic function.

When I visited Scotney a month after the storm, the drive was still lined on both sides with white moon-faces cut across the severed trunks of noble trees. The amount of work which had already been done was impressive, and workers were just struggling to re-erect the great lime tree, whose upper branches had been cut away like the top-hamper of a capsized ship. Its roots were so badly damaged that there was no hope of its surviving, but upright it would hint at the punctuation it had once provided in its corner of the lawn, and would serve as a memorial to itself – what Jeremy Bentham would have called an auto-eikon. Trees with no timber value lay sawn up nearby, as one sometimes sees the columns of classical temples demolished by earthquakes centuries ago: rows of drum-shaped blocks still lying leaning on one another in order.

Scotney is one of that knot of gardens which cluster near the middle of the Weald, on rising ground full in the path of the storm. There can scarcely have been such a concentration of green archives of gardening history anywhere in the world.

Nymans, Chartwell, Chevening, Hever, Chiddingstone, Bateman's, Bodiam, Leeds, Alfriston, Wych Cross and Polesden Lacey, Sheffield, Penshurst, Ightham and Knole – their names offer the raw material for an elegy on fallen trees like that plangent catalogue of defunct country railway stations that Flanders and Swann used to sing. Each one had a story more or less like that of Scotney – considerably more, in the case of Emmetts, say; in the case of Vita Sackville-West's long-elaborated garden at Sissinghurst ("not a tree garden"), markedly less. The caprice of the gale left a few famous woods scarcely touched at all: Gilbert White's hangar wood at Selborne for instance.

At Sheffield Park in east Sussex, another of Capability Brown's compositions, 80 per cent of the mature trees came down in some areas, including three giant Australian eucalyptus and a venerable Monterey pine which in the miserly way characteristic of its species had been nursing some of its pine cones on its branches for as long as 40 years. I saw the garden's famous alley of autumn gentians just coming into flower, unaffected as yet by the decimation overhead of the wood which had sheltered them.

At Nymans, they had 28 trees which were "champions" – the tallest or the largest in girth recorded of their kind. Only eight of them survived. The largest monkey puzzle in the country was one that did not. At the Royal Horticultural Show soon after, Nymans entered a display made up of foliage from 40 different species of conifers felled by the storm, and won a Gold Medal: a posthumous decoration.

Wakehurst, the outpost in the Weald of the Royal Botanical Gardens, lost half its important trees. Standen lost its famous mulberry tree, and the beeches of Slindon Wood were scattered like matchsticks.

The wind seemed to take a particular glee in seeking out the former homes of prime ministers (or, not to anthropomorphise, it caught out the tendency of former prime ministers to take a particular glee in settling in these particularly pleasant and convenient acres). Churchill's great horseshoe of beeches framing the view across the lake at Chartwell were mown down; so was the handsome park where Disraeli used to play the exotic aristocrat at Hughenden. The 900-acre woodlands at Birchgrove which were the special pride of Harold Macmillan, who had died ten months before, suffered 60 per cent damage: 60,000 trees were destroyed and 10,000 more were so badly damaged that their long-term survival was in doubt.

Scotney itself had for many years been a weekend home for another prime minister, Margaret Thatcher, although she had given up her flat there shortly before the storm. However, it was noted that the storm had not been rash enough to misbehave in Downing Street.

In the Chelsea Physic Garden, it was under no such inhibition. Duncan Donald, curator of the garden, had been roused in the night by one of the trees in his charge (*Gleditsia triacanthos x. inermis*) crashing through the roof of his house. The garden was founded by the Apothecaries' Company in 1673, "for the manifestation of the glory . . . of God", and to grow herbs , spices and other useful plants. It was visited by all the botanical founding fathers, including John Evelyn, Sir Joseph Banks (who sailed with Captain Cook) and the great Linnaeus. Planted outside London, it was long ago swallowed up in its growth, but had remained as it was, open on a restricted basis, and with its trees shutting out the sights and sounds of the city, as if London had not really stretched out to envelop it at all.

When light came, Mr Donald went out to inspect the damage, and found many of the garden's most venerable trees laid flat. Perhaps the greatest loss was a giant holm oak about 250 years old, probably the oldest tree in the garden. A 200-year-old plane fell across the roof of the Bargehouse, in which the Apothecaries used in the past to keep the four-oared livery boat in which members of the Company were conveyed in pomp to and from their Hall at Blackfriars.

Even in the confined enclosure of the garden, the wind had contrived to leave its special signature of a corridor of extra devastation. Four of Mr Donald's favourite trees had come down in a run: a golden false acacia, a cucumber tree, a tulip tree – and the thornless honey locust tree which had burst through his roof.

But the garden's old yew tree (a shallow-rooted species) was still standing, and so was the largest olive tree in England, which still bears fruit. The newly-rebuilt greenhouses (the first heated greenhouse in Britain was built here in 1681) were untouched.

"We may be temporarily dismayed, but we are not devastated", says Mr Donald. "Since the storm we have had a stream of timber connoisseurs, from wood carvers to cabinet makers, who were delighted at the unexpected opportunity to acquire some unusual timber for their crafts."

Scholarly gardens of this kind have a value quite distinct from their role as pleasant places to walk a pram. The Chelsea Physic Garden is still a centre of active research as well as a living catalogue of plants with medical or culinary uses. Major specimens may not only be rare and hard to replace, but may have a position as exemplary and representative individuals, Platonic trees, with a status a little like that of those bronze sets of standard weights, troy and avoirdupois, cast for Elizabeth I and stamped with her initial and the date 1582, and kept at the Tower of London for lesser weights to be measured against.

Important as the Physic Garden is in this respect, it is little more than a backwater compared to the Royal Botanical Gardens at Kew. Kew is a national institution, in a sense that none of the other historic places afflicted by the storm quite equals. The headlines put it at the time that it was as if St Paul's had received a direct hit in the blitz: it was more as if the British Museum had been hit.

An inventory of the harm done to the country's definitive botanical collection would be a scholarly treatise in itself; an excellent preliminary summary by Stephanie Pain appeared in *New Scientist* seven weeks after the disaster. All I can do is pick out a few details indicating some of the types of problem that the staff of the gardens faced when they arrived in the morning, past the row of levelled horse chestnuts in Kew Green, to start to assess the damage.

They found about 500 trees fallen, 500 more badly damaged. William IV's temple was carrying the weight of its lifelong partner, the Tree of Heaven, an unusually fine specimen. Fortunately there had been no other serious damage to the garden's collection of picturesque and functional buildings (some of them significant pieces of architecture in their own right) which protect from the English climate plants so fragile that one night of exposure might prove fatal.

· The avenue of 16 tulip trees along the Broad Walk (after 50 years just reaching the age at which the species begins to put out dense flowers) had lost five of its members, and two more were in too bad a state to be left standing. The matched trees of many species lining the Pagoda Vista had been lopsidedly lopped in a similar fashion.

The prominent turkey oak beside the pond, mentioned in the last chapter, had pitched in among the ornamental carp. The headache tree (not a curer but a causer of headaches, with the smell of its crushed leaves) had been the finest specimen in the country and had provided shelter for a grouping of Mediterranean plants around it, which would now be exposed. The Himalayan elm had fallen too. It had survived the Dutch Elm Disease epidemic and had a significant place in the international research programme to breed an elm resistant to the disease.

The oldest fallen tree whose exact age was known was an Iranian elm, planted in 1761. But a sweet chestnut also went down which might have been more than 300 years old, a relic of the woods that grew at Kew before Princess Augusta, George III's mother, began to make "a garden for pleasure" there in 1759.

"This is the worst day in the entire history of Kew", Alan Beyer, deputy curator of the gardens, told Alan Hamilton of *The Times* that morning. "It is impossible to put any kind of financial valuation on the damage".

He had worked at Kew for his entire career, and was looking at his life's work largely destroyed in a single night. Even disregarding irreplaceable historic trees, it was likely to be at least 20 years before the scientific wounds in the collections could be healed, and a century or more before the appearance of the gardens would again be comparable to what it had been the night before.

The gardens had to be completely closed for 12 days, and remained partially closed for many months longer, until all areas could be made safe. In an ordinary park, trees which have lost a limb or two are a matter of no more than minor aesthetic regret, once they have been made safe. In a garden of standard specimens, each individual and group is planted so that the trees can express their nature most fully, without being manipulated (as happens very often) to create an artificially graceful effect, or to produce straight timber. Even the natural vicissitudes of a storm impair this attempt to produce a representative tree, and many of the damaged trees at Kew are now a little less themselves, from the botanical point of view, than they used to be.

Nor can Kew go to the nurseryman round the corner to order replacement saplings. It has its own facilities for propagation and research, and cuttings have been taken from the fallen trees. But elderly trees do not graft well. Only trees of well-documented provenance are acceptable as scientific specimens. In some cases, as with the Iranian and Himalayan elms, it would be almost impossible today to obtain a replacement from their native habitats: for political reasons in one case, and because the tree has grown scarce even at home in the other.

Like the trees at Burnham Beeches, the Kew casualties are having their roots examined for biochemical traces. A major pharmaceutical company has taken samples, especially of the rarer species where the chance to make such a study seldom arises, to see whether fungi living in a symbiotic relationship with them might have medical properties never identified before.

Tree planting must be carefully paced. Young trees need more care than mature ones, and the gardeners can manage only a limited number at one time. If the cycle of replacement is not spread evenly over the years, then whole sections of the gardens might tend to come due for replacement *en masse* sometime in the future.

One casualty of the storm seems to have been doomed to persistent bad luck. It is a Japanese cedar which was planted by the Emperor of Japan on his state visit to Britain in 1971. The visit by the man who had been titular ruler of Japan during the war stirred up bitter memories. The night after the tree was planted, it was secretly uprooted. Carefully replanted, it was reduced by the storm to something resembling a fence-post, with all its branches snapped off, and its survival must be very doubtful.

And as the shredders noisily began to reduce to sawdust trees which had been types of their kind the night before, Michael King, the secretary of the gardens, sent a message of condolence to break the news to the Queen that the English walnut she had planted in 1959, to celebrate the 200th anniversary of the gardens, was no more.

CHAPTER 21

OAKS FROM ACORNS

*"There are two sorts of efficiency: that of the typhoon and that
of the sap".*

(Albert Camus)

"The Met Office said there would be no hurricane, and there was no hurricane", the director general of the Meteorological Office had said. Dr Houghton was in the strictest sense correct. Hurricanes, in the primary meaning of the word, are a particular kind of tropical storm which by definition cannot happen in latitudes like ours, where the sea is never warm enough to stoke them up. Whipped up partly by the after-currents of Hurricane Floyd, our storm might claim to be a hurricane's nephew or niece, but not the thing itself.

The first Spanish and Portuguese voyagers so clearly recognised these storms as something altogether outside European experience that they adopted the name for them used by the Carib Indians (by the men of the tribe, that is. Carib was a tongue perhaps unique in that it was only spoken by males: the women of the tribe spoke Arawak, the language of a conquered enemy).

But as far as ordinary users are concerned, the dictionary gives us ample sanction to call what happened on October 16 a hurricane. "A name given primarily to the violent windstorms of the West Indies . . .", the Oxford Dictionary rules, ". . . hence, any storm or tempest in which the wind blows with terrific violence". Shakespeare himself uses the word in this looser sense; so did Burke, and several of the correspondents quoted by Defoe.

The head of the Met Office may quite properly seek to set a higher standard of precision in these matters than Shakespeare. But the word is not quite straightforward, even in meteorological usage. A wind of Force 12 on the Beaufort scale is officially listed as "Hurricane". The criteria for a wind of hurricane force are specific: the speed has to be an average of 73 mph or more measured over ten minutes, at a given height above the ground. Brief gusts of greater strength are not uncommon, and the wind always blows stronger high in the air than near the surface. Weathermen are rightly disdainful of headline-writers who cheapen the name by using it whenever that happens.

It must have seemed virtually inconceivable at the time that a storm in south-east England could ever pass the ten-minute test. When Dr Houghton spoke, detailed reports from all weather stations had still not been fully analysed, and his words reflect that natural professional disdain. But in fact, the strict test had been passed in at least three places: at Gorleston in Norfolk (77 mph) and at Dover and Shoreham by Sea (85 mph). There, at least, it had blown a hurricane incontestably.

Not that the eager arguments over the point at the time stood a single tree up again, or rebuilt one chimney pot. But it was widely felt to be a matter of acute significance, because only the superlative could mark out the experience as something truly extraordinary. If one had to loose one's roof, it was some consolation to have lost it to something more than a storm. The general consciousness of having passed through an exceptional visitation needed to be sanctioned by a name.

All this was acutely irritating to Scots and Northerners. Hurricane force winds are two a penny in Scotland: they have been recorded there three times in the last 40 years. Out in Caithness the trees regularly go down like skittles in the winter (that is why Caithness is such a very unsuitable place for today's princely state incentives inducing people to plant them there). Northerners derived some satisfaction from declaring that the whole to-do only proved yet again how effete southerners beyond the Trent really were – and how utterly committed the national media were to the theory that nothing mattered unless it happened in London.

The Whitehall press conference held in February to release the two official reports on the storm – one of those pieces of funereal pomp designed to bury a subject as a live political issue – was curiously dominated by several irascible Scots. They seemed much crosser about the affair than the London press, who were tending to smirk up at the paintings of Nelson and other bemedalled heroes hanging in the Ministry of Defence's grand lobby, and reflect that it was October 16 which had enrolled them as heroes too. The more the Scots felt the weight of the surrounding post-Blitz spirit, the more sharply they demanded assurances that the Met Office should allow no more hurricanes for another 300 years.

Of course the wind was less exceptional by Scottish standards than English ones. The strongest gust ever recorded in these islands remains the 172 mph measured on Mount Cairngorm in 1986, at an altitude of 4,084 feet. But velocity is not the only thing that counts. The pressure-gradient which generated the winds was not only the steepest ever recorded in Britain, but effectively half as large again as the steepest recorded previously. Statistical probabilities suggest an even chance that the same thing will not happen again for 500 years. Several weather stations recorded gusts which are unlikely to recur at those spots for at least 200 years.

On any measure of grief and loss, the storm of 1987 was beyond all contention the most serious to have struck these islands since 1953. The wind may blow stronger further north, but the north has always been more ready for it. There are no stands of graceful shallow-rooted beeches to be swept away in Caithness, because the winds would have them out of the ground before they could put out a leaf. A bull in a china shop is news: a bull on a heath is not. Southern England is one of the world's china shops, and much pretty crockery got smashed there that night.

The Association of British Insurers estimates that approximately one insured household in six in southern England suffered significant damage. Presumably the proportion among uninsured homes was about the same. More than 1.2 million claims were received, and £850 million was paid out, three-quarters of it in domestic claims. Considering that more than a third of householders are uninsured, the damage actually suffered must have been well over £1,000 million.

To add other categories of loss to such a huge figure is like adding teaspoonfuls to a bucket. But local authorities had spent almost £100 million on relief by early March. The Ministry of Defence, one of the country's largest landowners, faced a bill of £15 million for repairs, excluding losses in its forestry holdings. The National Health Service's cash limit for the year was raised by £13.3 million to allow for storm damage. British Rail was estimated to have lost at least £1.5 million.

As for the value of the 15 million lost trees, one is quickly lost in semantics if one tries to estimate it. Owners had lost outright their actual planting costs, and would have to clear the devastated ground before they could plant again (clearance being considerably more costly than planting in these conditions). They had also lost the potential market value of those trees, the great majority of which were now valueless, and whatever fiscal rewards they might have looked forward to for planting them. From the taxpayer's point of view, the last point might count rather as a gain than a loss. As for timber which would normally have been of commercial value, there was so much of it that the glut distorted the market. But the overall loss of value must be counted in tens of millions at least.

There has been nothing to compare with the cost of the 1987 storm in Britain in modern times. The severe snowstorms at the beginning of the year left an insurance bill of almost £300 million. For the freeze and floods of 1981–2 (much more widespread than the 1987 storm) the bill was £324 million (allowing for changes in the purchasing power of the pound). Even the great east-coast floods of February 1953 caused insured losses of only about £400 million, in comparable terms. (Of course this excludes the cost of improving sea defences so as to ensure that nothing of the kind happened again).

Another way of assessing a pecking-order among storms would be to count how many people they killed. By this measure, the 1953 floods dominate the reckoning as unassailably as 1987 dominates the table of cash losses. The official death-toll in England was 307 – excluding at least 120 deaths at sea, and almost 1,500 in the Netherlands. The floods were indirectly caused by the wind, for the high tides would not have burst the sea walls if they had not been heaped up higher than usual by storms – eight feet higher than their expected level in places.

In this context, the striking thing about 1987 was not how many died, but how few. The best figure for those killed in Britain on the night, and those who died later of injuries sustained then, seems to be 19. Four more died while helping to clear the wreckage, and seven other storm and flood deaths followed in the next three days, in the fall-out from Hurricane Floyd. In addition, deaths in France were variously reported at two or four, there was one death in the Netherlands, and about 16 died in Spain and Portugal.

The exact number is another of those questions, like the value of fallen trees, which fades away into semantics: I gave up trying to reach certainty after considering the case of a lady in north London who was roused by the storm and killed by falling downstairs, but was found to have had a high level of alcohol in her blood; that of a dairyman near Godalming, battered to death by an intruder during a power cut; and that of a man near Woking, crushed by a storm-damaged tree he was trying to fell four months after the storm (clearing up was a process which took very much longer than four months before it was anything like complete). These deaths are omitted from all lists, and understandably so, though it is likely that all three would still be alive if it had not been for the storm.

Even put at its highest, the death toll in Britain was remarkably small. This was mainly because the storm struck deep in the night, and possibly also because the forecasters gave no reason for people to look out for anything special. What the casualties would have been like if the storm had arrived at the height of the rush-hour can scarcely be imagined.

As life-threatening disasters go, the storm hardly rates mention. Three relatively run-of-the-mill storms in January and February, 1988, took another 17 lives. The Zeebrugge ferry disaster and the fire in King's Cross underground station took 193 and 30 lives respectively in the year of the storm. In the Caribbean and the Bay of Bengal hurricanes regularly leave casualties numbered not in tens, but in thousands. As I write, the papers are reporting with rather small headlines a landslide in the suburbs of Rio de Janeiro in which at least 300 have died; it seems unlikely that the authorities will ever trouble to ascertain the full number. In such contexts, it seems almost an impertinence to be writing about our own local mishap.

A disaster also has costs which are not easily measured in statistics. The long-term psychological effects on victims who may be physically quite unhurt, are too easily overlooked, and can be severe. Many of the survivors of the Zeebrugge disaster still needed counselling a full year afterwards. Six months after the storm, five-year-old Harriet Winder still felt nervous if she was in a car driving under trees, and still had a bed permanently made up in her parents' room so that she could come and join them whenever the wind got up. Double glazing and a soundproof door had been installed in her room when the house was repaired, but it is impossible to eliminate the sound of the wind in an old house with timber frames.

Six-year-old Clowey Bardell was beginning to get over her similar fears six months afterwards. Wendy, her mother, who had been woken from sleep with blood streaming from several cuts around the head, had taken the change in the family's life more or less in her stride. They were still living in a flat in Sevenoaks. The repairs on their home were expected to cost up to £100,000, and were unlikely to be complete until a full year after the storm. It was Trevor Bardell who proved to have been the most shaken in the family.

"I've always been a jovial person and bounced along, but it's virtually destroyed me", he said in April. "For 37 years my aims in life had been to get a nice house and cars and so on for the family. I had done it, too. Now we've lost all that. It has taken the wind out of my sails, and made me ask: 'What's it all about? There must be something more in life than this'.

"I'm giving up my business and looking for salaried work. We're not going back to the house even when its mended, but until it's finished we can't sell it and get away. Two weeks after the storm, the car was written off, too. It wasn't anybody's fault, it just hit the kerb. But it makes you think 'Maybe there's someone up there who doesn't like me' ".

Whoever writes the history of the Rio mudslide may well be writing a necessary book, which I do not think this one can claim to be: but he will not have as much fun as I have had. The storm of '87 was one of those events which rings right through society. It touched the country's political, administrative, productive, historical and domestic life in a hundred different ways. It was the kind of test which brings out the character of a society and makes it look at itself. What other subject could touch on the topics of meteorology, botany, global stock markets, structural dynamics, immigration, landscape painting, navigation, falconry, obstetrics and rate support grant – or bring butterflies, dinosaurs, juggernauts, Cabinet ministers, cowboys, schoolchildren, skeletons, brides and babies into a relationship together?

The questions it raised will be debated for years. It has already generated five official reports at least. It has filled 82 columns of Hansard. Reports by non-governmental bodies, histories, special supplements, special pleadings, action packs and souvenir editions fill a lengthy shelf.

Britain's emergency services, with their dispersed chain of responsibility, coped admirably with this dispersed, low-technology crisis. But would they cope as well with a Zeebrugge disaster (handled by the Belgians with autocratic efficiency) or a major nuclear hazard? Sooner or later, we shall find out. Is an agriculture as dependent as ours on artificial inputs and public subsidy sustainable in the long run? How much do we care about our woodlands? Was the Government right in its privatisation plan to disregard the Central Electricity Generating Board's masterly handling of the crisis? We are unlikely to find out before everybody concerned has retired.

Was the storm the harbinger of long-term climatic changes which may make such events more common? By burning fossil fuels and keeping huge herds of cattle which emit methane into the atmosphere day and night, man is gradually increasing the quantity of carbon dioxide in the air around the world. He is also cutting down on a huge scale the trees which can change the gas back into oxygen again. The exact implications of the carbon dioxide "greenhouse effect" are very uncertain, but they could well include more droughts in North Africa, and a milder, stormier climate in Britain.

Meteorologists play up this risk or play it down according to temperament. By its nature, the world's climate is inherently wayward and unpredictable. It is not possible to say with any certainty that the odd weather of 1987 and 1988 has been an early sign of more permanent changes. But the possibility cannot be ruled out that by the end of the century we may look back on October 16, 1987, as the day we started to learn to live in a greenhouse world.

As far as trees are concerned, the storm's unprecedented and harrowing losses once again look incidental on the larger stage. Acid rain, a progressive and man-induced malady, is in the process of killing Europe's trees in numbers which make 15 million seem a handful. In Switzerland, no fewer than 56 per cent of the country's trees are affected to some degree, and plans for a rescue project are expected to cost £100 million in that small country alone. In the rain forests of the tropics, the felling of trees is said to be proceeding all the time at a rate of 50 acres a minute – an environmental idiocy beside which all Europe's misfortunes must appear marginal.

It was not the worst disaster in the world, but it was ours. Perhaps because the largest number of casualties were not human but symbolic, not people but trees, we were able to immerse ourselves all the more freely in the sense of fundamental upheaval. It is a common theme in science fiction to trace how a change in some everyday aspect of the natural world might bring society to its knees: as in *The Birds*, or *The Death of Grass*. This was the Death of Trees, or the night the trees turned on us. For a moment society really did feel like a fragile skin stretched across the surface of those natural forces which can obliterate whole populations with indifference. That deep impulse to tease nature by surviving at the edge of things was obscurely satisfied in many of those who cut their way through a primal wilderness which had been re-created overnight, or endured a life (which proved to have its own unexpected rewards) cut off from many of the civilised services we have come unthinkingly to count on.

Most of all, it stirred us into a recollection of what trees mean to us. For thousands of years people worshipped them, made sacrifices to them, feared them (or the wolves and wodwos they might harbour) harvested them, depended on them in the most intimate and continuous way. It would be odd if that had not left some sort of trace in the common psyche. They remain our great refuge from the tyranny of the rectangle in the environments we construct for ourselves.

The fallen trees made us feel pity for our great wrinkled tribal elders, innocent of malice, silent observers of history five or ten generations beyond our memory. But we also felt a frisson of betrayal, as if some elephantine species we had used time out of mind as a humble beast of burden – marching it in ranks up hill and down dale, and slaughtering it without a qualm when it was fully fattened up – had suddenly turned dangerous. It is a deep habit to look at trees anthropomorphically: when pictures were shown on the television of bushes being fed into the chipping-machine at Kew, preparatory to being recycled as mulch or a soft surface to footpaths, viewers telephoned to protest indignantly: hadn't they suffered enough?

The trees themselves were indifferent. Thomas Hardy, an acute observer of the characters of trees, describes how in a gale "the lowest portions of their trunks, that had hardly ever been known to move, were visibily rocked by the fiercer gusts, distressing the mind with its painful unwontedness, as when a strong man is seen to shed tears".

But walking among the ravaged hulks of the victims after the storm, the anthropomorphist would not have been aware of any such sense of stress or pain. In defeat, there was still the sense of serene submission to events which even an oak expresses in the last resort. Trees are less concerned than we are with individual fate, and live to a different time-scale. It is as if to their bovine consciousness, the destruction of a copse in one spot and the growing of another on the other side of a valley, are events comparable to what we perceive when we see a herd of cows grazing up under the hill in the morning, and down by the lake in the afternoon. Our perception is too impatient to see that it is all much the same.

Hardy also tells a story which catches that sense of identification which underlay the pang we felt on October 16. In *The Woodlanders*, the old woodman John South grows obsessed with the elm tree (it would be an elm) which overshadows his cottage. "He says it is exactly his age, it has got human sense, and sprouted up when he was born on purpose to rule him and keep him its slave."

The old man lives in terror that it will fall at any moment and put an end to him. The rational doctor decrees that his obsession can only be cured by felling the tree ("What's a tree beside a life?"). Giles Winterbourne stealthily chops the elm down in the night (we have seen instances where a tree has fallen just outside a window and gone unheard; and perhaps the old man was deaf). In the morning John South sees that the tree is gone, and is overcome with speechless horror: he is dead by nightfall.

Even so, I believe that for most of us the perceived loss will disappear more quickly than we might like to think. Strangers looking around to see an England stripped flat will wonder what all the fuss was about. Even at Petworth, Scotney and Kew, the scars will heal so that soon only the attentive eye will be able to detect the difference.

Not that the storm will then be forgotten. On the contrary, it is already plain that it is well on the way into folklore, and will reappear in reminiscence, controversy, fiction and autobiography for decades to come. It is destined to be one of those occasional events – the death of President Kennedy is the most quoted example – where everyone is said to remember just what they were doing at the time. Research has shown that these memories are in fact erroneous to a quite startling degree, and it will no doubt be the same with the storm a quarter of a century hence. But the events of October 16, 1987, will go a progress through the imaginations of the populace, turning into something rich and strange as they do so.

I am myself in possession of a memory – which no scientific scepticism could possibly shake – of helping to celebrate VE Day in 1945 by hanging a Union Jack from my bedroom window, with little sandbags sewn into its corners to stop it tangling over the flag-pole. Most of us keep in mind a particular earliest memory which happens to be identifiable with some outside event that can be dated. For a very large number of children, the storm will occupy that place. For younger ones, there will be the sensation of being allowed to scramble on the rutted bark of some immense fallen trunk; for older ones, the adventure of being cut off from civilisation, or the glory of an unexpected day with no school. For a few, like Harriet Winder and Clowey Bardell, the memory will be one of real danger and terror.

Early in December, the town of Sevenoaks held a fair, or rather a Fayre, on the cricket-ground, to celebrate the planting of a row of seven young sessile oaks to replace the oaks blown down by the hurricane. A lively trade was done in small souvenirs carved from the fallen trees (which, being Turkey oaks, proved to be of negligible value as timber). Action replays of the disaster were shown in the video tents, and greatly enjoyed. Municipal and television celebrities wielded spades to enact symbolically the already-accomplished act of planting. Some 15,000 people turned up, and contributed £22,000 for the local replanting fund. It was so much fun that there was talk of making it an annual event.

There will be many children who remember that, too. "There is no error more common", affirms Repton, "than to suppose that the planter may not live to see . . . the beauty of his trees". The children who played among the tents on the day of Hurricane Fayre will be able to bear memories of the occasion, and of the disaster that gave rise to it, into the middle years of the next century. In 60 years' time, they should be able to see the oaks which have been planted to stand in the places of the victims of the storm grown to a height of 70 feet, and just entering upon their prime.

RECORDS OF WIND FROM WEATHER STATIONS ACROSS SOUTHERN ENGLAND, OCTOBER 16, 1987

Station	Highest mean deg/kn	Time GMT	Highest gust deg/kn	Time	Gust ratio
Amersham, Bucks	180/36	0200	180/73	0225	2.3
Ashford, Kent*	190/38E	0400	/92	0440	2.4
Boscombe Down, Wilts	170/37	0100	170/70	0114	1.9
Coltishall, Norfolk	190/44	0400	180/71	0400	1.6
Culdrose, Cornwall	350/48	0000	350/72	0020	1.5
Gatwick, Surrey	210/34	0400	210/86	0430	2.5
Gorleston, Norfolk	/66	0400	/106	0424	1.6
Guernsey Airport	250/55	0200	250/81	0218	1.5
Heathrow NE Site	170/43	0200	170/80	0240	1.9
Hemsby, Norfolk	190/48	0500	190/79	0420	1.6
Herstmonceux, Sussex	200/60E	0400	200/90	0455	(1.5)
Jersey Airport	220/55	0100	200/85	0102	1.5
Langdon Bay, Kent	180/54	0300	180/94E	0342	1.7
	190/56	0400	190/94	0448	1.7
	200/53	0500	210/94	0530	1.8
London, Post Office Tower	170/54	0200	170/94	0248	1.7
London Weather Centre	180/40	0200	180/82	0248	2.1
Manston, Kent	210/58	0400	210/86	0436	1.5
Middle Wallop, Hants	/48	0100	/78	0122	1.6
Norwich, Norfolk	210/34	0600	/74	0416	
Odiham, Hants	170/40	0100	180/70	0100	1.7
Portland Bill, Dorset	260/52	0300	270/78	0348	1.5
Portland RNAS, Dorset	270/55	0300	260/86	0318	1.6
Sheerness, Kent	200/63	0400	200/93	0430	1.5
Shoeburyness, Essex	230/56	0400	210/87	0443	1.6
Shoreham by Sea, Sussex*	220/74	0300	220/98	0310	1.3
			220/98	0330	1.3
			/100E		
Southampton, Hants	170/30	0200	170/75	0215	2.5
Thorney Island, Sussex*	200/59	0300	210/90	0342	1.5
Wattisham, Suffolk	180/35	0300	180/72	0342	2.1
	200/44	0500	220/70	0502	1.6
	220/46	0600	220/70	0622	1.5

E denotes an estimated value
* indicates an interrupted record

To the left: compass angle, speed in knots, and time, of strongest ten-minute bursts from each station. In centre, compass angle, speed and time of highest recorded short gusts. To right, "Gust Ratio": disproportionately intense gusts marked by high ratios.

CREDITS

INDEX

Page numbers in bold indicate a photograph or diagram reference.